D1495927

THE FIRST GENERAL AVIATION AIRPLANE
Kitty Hawk, December 1903

"We shall have an entirely new form of transportation which will serve many ends and contribute in many ways to the welfare and happiness of mankind."

— Orville Wright

The Safe and Useful Aeroplane
Harper's Magazine, April 1917

SAFETY

IN

GENERAL AVIATION

Harold D. Hoekstra
Shung-chai Huang

December 1971

Flight Safety Foundation, Inc.
Arlington, Virginia
U.S.A.

FOREWORD

Flight Safety Foundation is pleased to present this first authoritative overall study of safety in general aviation. It is particularly fitting that the sponsor is one who contributed much to early progress in general aviation and whose present detachment from aviation contributes objectivity and perspective to this work.

We believe that this wide-ranging yet concise study, covering aircraft, airmen and operations including regulatory, production, safety statistics, crashworthiness, and research and development standpoints, will assist in the development of improved safety and, in turn, utility of general aviation.

This study confirms the fact that the pilot is and will remain the prime element in maintaining and improving safety. However, the other elements of the aviation system must provide in increasing measure compensation for the limitations and failings of the human element.

DAVID D. THOMAS
President
Flight Safety Foundation

5-30-80

ACKNOWLEDGEMENTS

This study has been actively supported by Mr. Clayton J. Brukner of Troy, Ohio, a pioneer aviator, industrialist and philanthropist.

After nine years in aviation, Mr. Brukner and Mr. Elwood J. "Sam" Junkin founded the Waco Aircraft Company in 1923. By the late 1920's Waco airplanes had attained the highest production rate and number of any U.S. aircraft and had won many trophies for performance, including Ford Reliability Tours in successive years.

Brief outlines of the careers of both Brukner and Junkin appear on page 114 of this report.

Flight Safety Foundation also wishes to express appreciation to:

Mr. C. O. Miller, Director, Aviation Safety Bureau and members of his staff at the National Transportation Safety Board and in particular Mr. Forris M. Hollowell, Chief, Information Systems Branch, for their considerable assistance in providing and processing statistical information.

Mr. James Rudolph, Director, Flight Standards Service of FAA, and his staff for technical assistance.

Dr. Peter V. Siegel, Federal Air Surgeon, and members of his staff in Washington and Oklahoma City and particularly Dr. John J. Swearingen, Chief of the Protection and Survival Laboratory, for advice and data, and to

Mr. Jerome Lederer, Director of Safety, NASA and former President of the Society of Air Safety Investigators, for assistance with a questionnaire to the Society, and for his advice and counsel.

In addition, the Aircraft Owners and Pilots Association (AOPA) and members of the General Aviation Manufacturers Association (GAMA), including Beech Aircraft Corporation, Cessna Aircraft Company, Lycoming Division of AVCO, and Piper Aircraft Corporation provided certain information and statistical data.

The authors are indebted to D. N. Ahnstrom, Vice-President, Publications of Flight Safety Foundation, for invaluable editorial advice and assistance throughout the preparation and publication of this book.

The authors also wish to express their appreciation for information and suggestions from B. R. Allen, Raymond C. Blaylock, Silas Clark, Jeremiah Gerteis, Silvia Goring, Dudley Hill, Harvey Hansberry, Robert R. Osborn, Jean Roche, Stephen H. Rolle, Theodore Sanford and Paul Spiess. In addition thanks are due Flight Safety Foundation staff members for their assistance, and in particular Mrs. Marjorie Rodgers and Mrs. Nancy Harmon of the secretarial staff.

Library of Congress Catalog Card Number 73-186323
International Standard Book Number 0-912768-01-0

Printed in The United States of America
by Carman Printing Associates, Inc., New York

First Edition

First Printing, December, 1971

CONTENTS

1. INTRODUCTION

The objective of this study is to examine safety in general aviation through its evolution, the current record as revealed by statistics, and the design and operational means by which the record may be improved.

Early in 1970 the Flight Safety Foundation asked the aviation industry to state what in its view were considered to be the 10 most urgent safety problems in need of solution. The response from U.S. and foreign sources, including air carriers, corporate aircraft operators, Foundation members, NBAA members, military services and others, was most gratifying.[1]

After Air Traffic Control and Airports as first and second in order of priority came Regulations, including the certification of aircraft. Fourth and fifth were Pilot Technique and Training, and Weather respectively. Sixth was Aircraft Design, including "Aircraft equipment, uniformity of instrumentation, engineering, system safety concept including shoulder harness, padded instrument panel, recessed instruments."

The remaining four dealt with Maintenance, Human Factors, Rescue and Survival, and Communications and Navaids.

Increased emphasis on general aviation safety has been evidenced by the government. The NTSB has made recommendations to the FAA on improving crashworthiness standards,[2] and the FAA has outlined its actions and program to the NTSB.[3] Critical articles such as that by Anderson[4] as well as such constructive work as the voluntary accident prevention program initiated by the Federal Aviation Administration[5] have come to public attention. Flight Safety Foundation itself recently broadened its scope to provide safety information to the general aviation pilot.

Because of the importance of general aviation safety and the broad interest in it, Flight Safety Foundation has given priority to an objective study of the subject. In this study:

- Literature on the subject has been reviewed.

- Discussions have been held with key representatives of airframe producers, operators, users, insurors, accident investigators and others.

---

[1] FSF Flight Safety Facts and Analysis—August 1970.
[2] NTSB letter dated August 28, 1970, to FAA.
[3] FAA letter dated September 8, 1970, to NTSB.
[4] Jack Anderson "The Growing Menace of the Private Plane" - Parade Magazine, October 26, 1969.
[5] FAA Administrator Shaffer letter to all pilots, November 3, 1970.

- FAA medical and engineering records and tests at the FAA Aeronautical Center at Oklahoma City have been reviewed.

- Members of the Society of Air Safety Investigators have been canvassed to determine their views on crashworthiness.

- Some comparisons between automobile and aircraft production, crashworthiness and statistics have been included because of the relationships between these two modes of personal transportation and the problems common to both.

- Through the cooperation of the NTSB, machine runs of records, including the latest completely tabulated figures available, have been made on general aviation accidents, i.e.,

    a. Overall general aviation accident statistics for the calendar years 1959 through 1969, a total of 55,351 accidents of which 5,796 were fatal.

    b. All small fixed-wing aircraft accidents for the calendar years 1968 and 1969, a total of 9,124 accidents.

    These have been studied for trends, including fire and no-fire accidents, high-wing versus low-wing and single-engine versus multi-engine airplanes.

- Preliminary statistics for 1970 and available returns for 1971 from NTSB and FAA have been analyzed.

- Individual accident cases have been examined to provide detailed information on the causes of certain types of accidents.

Inasmuch as approximately 80% of the general aviation activity reported by ICAO nations takes place in the United States, most of the information shown in this report is based upon U.S. information. Information from non-U.S. sources is specifically indicated. Where appropriate, metric system units have been included to facilitate international use.

On the basis of the foregoing information and the technical studies which were made, conclusions have been formulated and are discussed in Chapter 10.

$\mathcal{2}_\circ$ DEFINITION OF GENERAL AVIATION

The International Civil Aviation Organization (ICAO) describes general aviation as the operation of aircraft owned by individuals or businesses and not as revenue-producing aircraft carrying passengers, cargo or mail. (ICAO Bulletin, October 1970).

The U.S. National Transportation Safety Board defines general aviation as "the operation of U.S. civil aircraft owned and operated by persons, corporations, etc., other than those engaged in air carrier operations authorized by a certificate of public convenience and necessity, issued by the Civil Aeronautics Board." (Ref. Annual Review of U.S. General Aviation Accidents − 1968).

The U.S. FAA defines general aviation operation as "all civil aircraft operations except those classified as air carrier."

In the regulatory field, such as the Federal Aviation Regulations (FARs) issued by the U.S. Federal Aviation Administration, the definition becomes more complex. *Figure 1* shows the categories and classifications of all uses of civil aircraft as defined in the airworthiness and operations sections of the U.S. Federal Aviation Regulations. Insofar as general aviation operations are defined it can be seen that the private owner or a corporation, for example, may employ large transport airplanes, helicopters or even free balloons as well as normal category airplanes.

The FAA Statistical Handbook of Aviation includes air taxi operation except for those carriers with specific schedules, defined by the CAB as commuter air carriers. On December 1, 1970 there were 176 of these.

In this study attention will be directed principally to normal category airplanes, both single-engine and light twins, mostly under 6,000 pounds (2,720 kg) maximum weight and none exceeding 12,500 pounds (5,670 kg) maximum takeoff weight. These airplanes constitute 97% or the vast majority of the civil aviation fleet.

Where significant differences from the above definitions appear in this report a suitable qualification is included.

Figure 1
CATEGORIES and CLASSIFICATIONS of CIVIL AIRCRAFT under the AIRWORTHINESS and OPERATIONS FEDERAL AVIATION REGULATIONS

AIRCRAFT CATEGORY AND CLASS	AIRWORTHINESS STANDARDS	WEIGHT RANGE	NUMBER OF PASSENGERS	NUMBER OF ENGINES REQUIRED	ONE-ENGINE-INOPERATIVE PERFORMANCE FOR MULTI-ENGINE AIRCRAFT			OPERATIONS FOR WHICH AIRCRAFT IS ELIGIBLE					
					TAKE-OFF	ENROUTE	APPROACH	GENERAL FAR 91	AIR TAXI & COMMUTER FAR 135	AIR CARRIER (1) FAR 121	AIR CARRIER (2) FAR 127	AGRICULTURAL & INDUSTRIAL FAR 137	FAR 133
TRANSPORT CATEGORY													
Airplanes	FAR 25	Unlimited	Unlimited	Multi	✓	✓	✓	✓	✓	✓		✓	
Rotorcraft Category A	FAR 29	A-Unlimited B-20,000# Max.	Unlimited	A-Multi B-Single or Multi	✓ —	✓ —	✓ —	✓	✓		✓	✓	
Category B	FAR 29											✓	
V/STOL	Tentative Standards verticraft/powered lift	Unlimited	Unlimited	Multi	✓	✓	✓	✓	✓	✓		✓	
SST	Tentative Standards	Unlimited	Unlimited	Multi	✓	✓	✓	✓	✓	✓			
NORMAL, UTILITY & ACROBATIC CATEGORIES													
Small Airplanes 12,500 lbs. Maximum	FAR 23; 23.1	12,500 lbs. Max.		Multi if V$_s$ over 70 mph	✓	✓	✓	✓	✓ if 9 pass. or less			✓	
6,000 to 12,500#	23.51, 23.65, 23.67 23.75, 23.77	6,000# to 12,500# Max.		Multi if V$_s$ over 70 mph		✓	✓	✓	✓ if 9 pass. or less			✓	
Stall speed over 70 mph	23.45(b); 23.67(b)(1)	12,500# Max.		Multi if V$_s$ over 70 mph	✓	✓	✓	✓	**			✓	
For Air Taxi 10 or more passengers	Appendix A FAR 135*	12,500# Max.	10 or more	Multi	✓	✓	✓	✓	✓ if 9 pass. or less			✓	
For all airplanes 10 or more passengers	Amendment 23-10***	12,500# Max.	10 or More	Multi	✓	✓	✓	✓	✓ if 10 pass. or more	✓		✓	
Rotorcraft	FAR 27	6,000# Max.		Single or Multi				✓	✓		✓	✓	
V/STOL (small)	Tentative Standards in preparation							✓	✓			✓	
RESTRICTED CATEGORY	FAR 21.25							✓				✓	
EXTERNAL LOADS	FAR 133(D)							✓					
GLIDERS	FAR 21.23							✓					
FREE BALLOONS	FAR 31							✓					
AMATEUR-BUILT	FAR 21.191(g)							✓					✓

* SFAR 23 used for type certification until 7/19/70
** Effective date, June 1, 1972
*** Amendment 23-10 effective March 13, 1971 requires type certification under FAR 25 for all new type 10 or more passenger airplanes
(1) Commercial Operators large aircraft included
(2) Helicopters

Metric Equivalents
6,000 pounds – 2720 kg
12,500 pounds – 5670 kg
20,000 pounds – 9080 kg
70 mph – 113 km/hr

LEVEL OF SAFETY — AIRCRAFT WEIGHT
NORMAL CATEGORY — 12,500 — TRANSPORT CATEGORY
Additional FAA Safety Rules
Additional CAB Economic Rules / Exemptions (A/C > 12,500 in Air Taxi)

Categories

Normal Category. Most general aviation activity is conducted with aircraft certificated in the normal category, the airworthiness standards for which appear in Federal Aviation Regulations Part 23. It is limited to airplanes intended for non-aerobatic operation and not exceeding 12,500 pounds (5,670 kg) in maximum takeoff weight. The standards specify minimum acceptable values for airframe strength, powerplant functioning and fire protection, detailed design, flight performance and flight characteristics.

Transport Category. Airplanes of any weight *may* be certificated in the transport category but all airplanes with a takeoff weight exceeding 12,500 pounds and used in the carriage of passengers or goods *must* be certificated in this category, covered by Federal Aviation Regulations Part 25. Transport airplanes must be multi-engine types. The airworthiness standards are considerably more detailed and rigorous than for the normal category in order to assure a higher level of safety for public transport for hire than for small aircraft primarily intended for private owner use.

Examples of the higher safety standards in Part 25 include:

a. Assured flight performance following failure of an engine,

b. Powerplant isolation, detection and extinguishing equipment for fire protection,

c. Passenger compartment fire-resistant interiors,

d. Impact-resistant windshields,

and other standards.

Many of the differences between Part 25 and Part 23 are necessary to provide for the greater size, weight, speed, complexity and more severe operating conditions of large transport airplanes.

When transport category airplanes are employed in scheduled operation, specific operational and maintenance procedures must be observed.

3. THE REGULATORY PROBLEM

The first airworthiness code for civil aircraft in the United States bore the date of December 31, 1926, and was identified as Air Commerce Regulations, Chapter 1, Licensing of Aircraft. A 17-page booklet it covered all requirements: structural, propulsion, flight test, licensing procedures for small and large aircraft, and other aspects.

For example, with respect to performance: ". . . the airplane must pass the following flight tests with full load:

1. Takeoff within 1,000 feet.

2. Climb at least 250 feet the first minute after taking off.

3. Land, coming to full stop without external aid, within 1,000 feet from point where wheels first touch the landing area.

With respect to restraint systems, the rule stated:

"Safety belts or equivalent apparatus for pilots and passengers in open-cockpit airplanes carrying passengers for hire or reward."

In other words, belts were required only if pay passengers were carried in open airplanes. Pay passengers in closed aircraft—no belt. Non-pay passengers in open aircraft—no belt.

There were no structural crashworthiness requirements, but because of the frequency of nose-over accidents with the conventional landing gear of that time, the main wheels being only slightly forward of the center of gravity, a nose-over design condition was specified. It was directed at preventing major damage to the airframe in the event of a nose-over at low speed. There appeared to be no concern regarding possible injury to the occupants.

In contrast with the 17-page booklet of 1926, the current standards (FARs) for both small and large airplanes:

Part 23 – Airworthiness Standards: Normal, Utility, and Acrobatic Category Airplanes, and

Part 25 – Airworthiness Standards: Transport Category Airplanes,

together with supplementary parts, encompass some 500 pages of fine print.

Obviously, the tremendous technical advances, the incorporation of many devices and systems into aircraft and the need to incorporate the lessons learned through experience are the major factors in the growth of the volume of airworthiness standards.

A further factor appears to be a continuing process of injecting legalistic complexity into what is basically an engineering and highly technical field. For example, as mentioned earlier Part 23 may be used for airplanes up to 12,500 pounds maximum weight, and Part 25, the transport category, must be used for all airplanes over 12,500 pounds maximum weight. In the civil air regulations, which were in effect from 1945 to 1965, Part 3, Normal Categories, page 1 (Section 3.0) states that "this part shall apply only to airplanes which have a maximum weight of 12,500 pounds or less." However, in the 1965 revision of this part and part 4b Transport Categories into the Federal Aviation Regulations, done by a legal group, there is no mention of weight limits in either of these parts. It is necessary to refer to a completely different section, Part 1 Definitions and Abbreviations, Section 1.1 and in the obscure location of the definition of "small airplane" the only reference to the 12,500-pound limit appears.

A similar growth and increase in complexity exists in the transport aircraft field as indicated by the following excerpt from an Aerospace Industries Association study.[6]

"The phenomenal growth of civil air transportation really began in the early 1930's when the DC-3 made its appearance. The DC-3 was a simple airplane, and the Airworthiness Standards of that day were also simple. A several page document called, 'Bulletin 7a' described the entire package for transport aircraft. Civil transport aircraft now come in all sizes and shapes. The reciprocating engine and propeller combination has been replaced largely by the jet. Shapes range all the way from a rotary wing aircraft to a supersonic transport. A rather dramatic size comparison is that the entire DC-3 fuselage could be nestled within the inlet duct of the Douglas DC-10 aft engine.

"Unfortunately, the size and complexity of the Federal Air Regulations for civil transport aircraft has more than kept pace with the size and complexity of the aircraft. Today the documentation is huge and, at the current rate of growth, the year 2,000 could see the engineer's office looking much like a lawyer's library."

At the end of World War II there was considerable pressure on the Department of Commerce and the Civil Aeronautics Administration, predecessors of the FAA, to transfer responsibility for the development and conformance to airworthiness standards of general aviation aircraft from the

---

[6]Application of New Concepts for Modernization of the Federal Air Regulations — Aerospace Industries Association, April 1970.

federal government to the industry itself. A number of aircraft companies were producing 30 to 50 airplanes per day and authoritative sources[7] estimated that there would be 400,000 registered civil aircraft in the U.S. by 1955 with an annual production of personal aircraft at that time of the order of 150,000 per year. The example of the automobile was used to illustrate the point on regulatory freedom. Here industry standards had been developed through the years and were met voluntarily or honored in the breach.

There was, however, objection in some quarters to relaxation in the administration of airworthiness standards. Some aircraft producers wanted the shelter of a federal approval in the event of liability suits. Others were concerned with unauthorized modification to their products. Some who had gone through engineering and testing to develop improvements to aircraft desired the strict certification rules and surveillance as protection against competition by those who would merely copy an existing article.

In 1947, the first step toward reducing federal involvement in general aviation took place with the establishment by the CAA of the delegation option, primarily through the initiative of Dr. T. P. Wright, then Administrator of the Civil Aeronautics Administration. By this means established airframe producers with one airplane type and production certificate to their credit could certify to the government that their aircraft met the required standards. Specific key individuals, such as the chief engineer, could sign such certification as a "designated engineering representative" (DER). The government retained the right to review and inspect or test any phase. Only minor changes have been made in this basic procedure since its inception.

The trend through the years has been toward increasing latitude for private venture and a theme of transfer of responsibility for standards to the industry. As a result government officials responsible for aircraft standards concentrated major attention and manpower to the problems of transport aviation used in the carriage of fare-paying passengers in public transport.

Now the pendulum is swinging again toward more firm and detailed federal surveillance of the entire transportation industry, both surface and air. The passage of the Transportation Act of 1966 brought many detailed standards into the automobile field. Public interest in having the federal government concern itself in more detail regarding the safety of general aviation aircraft is reflected in the Nader petition "to improve passenger safety in the event of a crash" submitted to the FAA on February 12, 1970 with an accompanying study[8] and the NTSB recommendations mentioned earlier (ref. 2).

---

[7]Dr. T.P. Wright, Personal Aircraft. Anglo-American Conference RAS-IAS September 1947, London.

[8]James Bruce and John Draper. Crash Safety In General Aviation Aircraft, January 1970.

In addition to the airworthiness phase of regulation, the operational, maintenance and economic aspects complicate the situation. *Figure 1,* discussed earlier, illustrates this. With respect to the economic phase the Civil Aeronautics Board generally has employed the 12,500-pound limit for air taxi or charter service and if a larger aircraft is to be employed "there must be a showing" such as needs or service to the community. Since 1965 the CAB has granted 87 out of 122 applications for exemption to permit the use of larger aircraft, and is considering changes to raise the 12,500-pound limit.[9]

Product liability insurance is that kind of insurance which provides protection against extraordinary losses resulting from defects or claims of defects in a manufacturer's products. The landmark case in U.S. jurisprudence was McPherson versus Buick in 1916 (217 New York 382). The principle of commercial fitness has since been adopted by most U.S. states in a uniform commercial code. The growth in product liability insurance rates in U.S. civil aviation is shown in *Figure 2.* This is another factor in generating the demand for stricter federal regulation, and also in increasing the cost of aircraft. Ironically, the alarming increase in rates, approximately three-fold between 1970 and those now required for 1972, has resulted from recent court awards, not from increased flight hazards. As shown by the supplementary curve on the same figure, safety is steadily improving — obviously the increase in liability insurance costs leads to increasing the cost of aircraft.

Legal aspects interfere with accident investigations and with the exchanges of safety information. Lederer has pointed out:[10]

"The rights of litigants that impede accident investigation also interfere with the free exchange of information that might prevent accidents or incidents. Much is being done, but much more is needed.

"Litigants have the right to subpoena the records and files of the manufacturers or any other organization involved in the accident. The potential defendants naturally become reluctant to voluntarily publish or report on their incidents or accidents as they have no way of controlling the subsequent use of this information in litigation. They can never be certain their legal defense will be adequate."

There has been a great increase in the extent of regulation and litigation pertaining to all phases of civil aviation and in a sense it has become a happy hunting ground for a portion of the legal profession.

---

[9] James Saltsman CAB, Business Aviation, December 28, 1970.
[10] Perspectives in Air Safety — Jerome Lederer. Daniel Guggenheim Medal Award Lecture, ASME, Washington, D.C. 1962.

Figure 2
PRODUCT LIABILITY INSURANCE RATES
AVERAGE VALUES

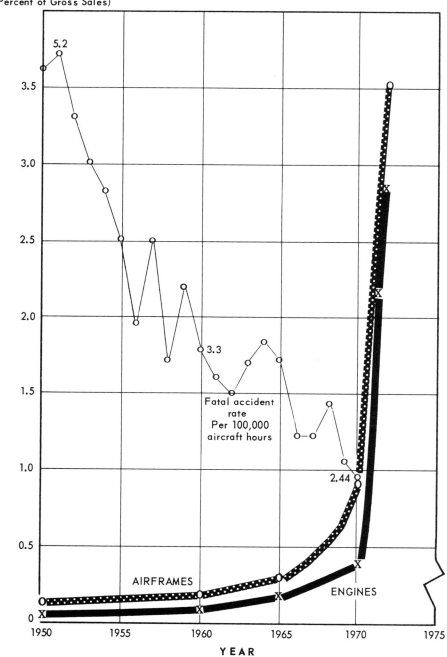

Insurance Rate
(Percent of Gross Sales)

AIRFRAMES

ENGINES

Fatal accident
rate
Per 100,000
aircraft hours

YEAR

Source: GAMA 1971

In summary, the legal profession has become much more deeply involved in aviation, part of it justified by the growth in cost, extent and complexity of aviation. In many areas, however, the legal intrusion brings complexity to the development of standards and compliance methods, hampers accident investigation and even the exchange of safety information. There is no question but that the cost of aviation has increased because of increased legal involvement.

A PRODUCTION AIRPLANE OF THE MID-1920's
The Waco 9

A PRODUCTION AIRPLANE OF THE EARLY-1970's
The Piper Cherokee

4. THE PRODUCTION PROBLEM

One of the problems in general aviation is the cost of designing, testing and producing airplanes in the relatively small quantities which the commercial market can absorb. Although the deliveries of U.S. general aviation fixed-wing aircraft in 1969 totaled 12,581 units, the deliveries in 1970 dropped to some 7,500 units. According to the General Aviation Manufacturers Association (GAMA), much of the decrease was attributable to the general economic situation. Early reports for 1971, however, indicated increased sales and deliveries.

In contrast, U.S. automobile and truck production was 10,182,562 in 1969 and 8,261,851 in 1970.[11]

This thousand-fold ratio permits the automobile producer to employ production techniques unthinkable for aircraft. In aircraft the very substantial design and testing costs must be spread over a relatively small number of units, and materials are purchased in small lots. In a few areas it is possible to take advantage of automobile volume prices. Automobile textiles for interior trim are used in some aircraft. Although seat belts were developed and used in airplanes much before they were adapted to automobiles, the latter types now are used extensively in aircraft.

As particular units are produced, direct labor costs should reduce as personnel become more familiar with the product and short cuts in the processes are developed. Various methods have been employed to predict savings but the most commonly employed is the "learning curve" concept. For example, if a 20% saving is achieved as the production quantity is doubled, it is referred to as an .8 or 80% learning curve. Hence, if the labor cost of producing the 10th unit is $100, the 20th should be $80, the 40th unit $64 and the 80th down to $51.20. Other factors, however, such as interruptions in production may negate the learning curve gains and increase costs.

Usual values for the learning curve range around 80% but the small volume of aircraft production limits its economic benefit.

With relatively limited funds it is most economical for aircraft producers to add power and increase payload and, incidentally, the takeoff weight of existing or slightly modified airframes. This provides greater speed and more capacity for payload or equipment with little change in tooling or production. This trend generally is acceptable to the current clientele of experienced users. But with its requirement of experienced pilots it does not broaden the market nor, with the increase in wing loading and minimum speed, does it increase safety.

---

[11]Wards Automotive Reports — January 18, 1971.

Another trend of little merit is that of design changes for styling purposes, such as the use of swept tails and long flat pointed nacelles. Changes of this kind may increase sales for a period, like the tail fins for automobiles, but in the long run they may have an adverse effect. A swept tail at speeds below about 400 mph (650 kmh) is less efficient, both aerodynamically and structurally, than an unswept surface. A long flat nacelle may introduce vibration problems in the powerplant or make more difficult the attainment of acceptable low-speed control and stall characteristics.

Production and costs play an important part in the adoption of safety improvements. New developments to improve safety must be designed into aircraft, tested, produced and put into use before safety gains are realized. If the cost increments of such developments are large, few aircraft so improved are sold. If the use of costly safety developments is made mandatory, fewer aircraft may be sold and the extent of use of such developments, and hence the benefits of improved safety, is retarded. Therefore, developments which are simple, low in cost and readily integrated into production aircraft will yield the greatest gains in safety, particularly for the near future.

An encouraging indication of increasing interest in new approaches in airplane design is the research airplane on page 110, the Cessna XMC.

Production and use of general aviation aircraft constitute a vital element in the U.S. economy. Total annual production value in 1969 was well over one-half billion dollars. General aviation serves as a training ground and experience-builder for many airline and military ground and flight personnel. The aircraft are essential to many agricultural and industrial operations. U.S. exports of this highly visible product range between 2,000 and 3,000 units per year with a value of around $100 million.

A comparison of a large production general aviation airplane of the 1920 period with a present-day type, almost 50 years later, is shown on page 12.

$5._{\circ}$ GENERAL AVIATION STATISTICS

This section summarizes the principal statistics of general aviation, i.e., the number of aircraft and pilots, and the extent of use during the period 1959-69. Information has been drawn from FAA and NTSB sources as well as other work. Growth predictions and trends, where available, also are included. World-wide values, where shown, are primarily based on ICAO publications.

Aircraft Fleet

World-wide, general aviation aircraft increased from 104,958 in 1962 to 166,128 in 1969. The total increase was 61,170 or 58%, approximating 8% annually. It was noted, however, that the increase from 1968 to 1969 was lower than in previous years and the production data available further indicates that the rate of growth of the world-wide general aviation fleet declined again in 1970. Considering the different types of aircraft, it appears that the number of turbine-powered aircraft increased at a much higher rate than piston-engine aircraft but the latter category is still dominant. The rotary-wing aircraft increased at a somewhat higher rate than fixed-wing aircraft. However, rotorcraft account for only 2% of the total fleet. It is also estimated that the geographical distribution of general aviation aircraft is about 84% in North America, i.e., Canada, Mexico and the United States, 4% in Central and South America, 8% in Europe, and 4% in combined Asia, Africa, Australia and New Zealand. [a]

The U.S. general aviation fleet totaled 68,727 active aircraft[b] in 1959. This increased to 130,806 in 1969, and is expected to number 175,000 in 1975. The U.S. fleet constitutes about 78% of the world's total. *Figure 3* illustrates the values. Using 1959 as a base, over the past decade the annual increase rate in general aviation active aircraft has averaged about 9%. From 1970 to 1975 the average annual increase rate is expected by FAA to be 5.5%.

The joint DOT/NASA Civil Aviation Research and Development (CARD) Study[12] shows an expected growth rate of 5.3% per year, leading to 287,000 general aviation aircraft in 1985, flying approximately 57 million hours annually. This trend also is shown in *Figure 3*.

---

[a] The USSR and the Peoples Republic of China are not included in this ICAO data.
[b] Defined by FAA as one with a current airworthiness certificate.
[12] DOT/NASA Civil Aviation Research and Development (CARD) Policy Study — Supporting Papers. March 1971, Washington, D.C.

Figure 3

ACTIVE GENERAL AVIATION AIRCRAFT
ACTUAL AND FORECAST
1959 – 1975

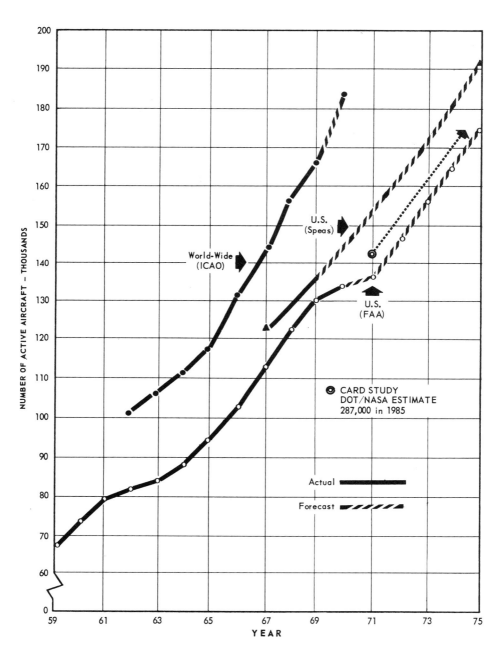

Number of Pilots

The data in *Figure 4* represents the number of active pilots in the United States, i.e., those with current certificates, as carried in the FAA airmen certification records. It shows 359,875 active pilots in 1959, decreased to 348,062 in 1960, apparently due in part to the slow down of the nation's economy. The total then rather steadily increased to 720,028 in 1969. Over this period, the total increase rate was more than 100%, or more than 10% per annum. Another period of relatively slow growth is shown in the 1969–1970 period, again probably related in part to the sluggish economy. According to FAA forecast, the growth in aviation activities will have regained its momentum in 1971, and the number of U.S. pilots is expected to be 1,013,200 in 1975.

According to ICAO information, the number of private pilots in ICAO contracting states, which was estimated at 410,000 for 1968, increased to 450,000 in 1969, and 470,000 in 1970. This represents an increase of about 10% over 1968 and only 4% over 1969. In 1970 there were about 300,000 student pilots in ICAO contracting states which issue such licenses.

AOPA figures for world-wide general aviation show 1,005,100 pilots in December 1969. No trend information is available.

Hours Flown

Information relating to the annual hours flown for world-wide general aviation in the early 1960's is not available. According to ICAO, the number of hours flown in 1970 by general aviation aircraft in ICAO contracting states, exclusive of the USSR, increased little over 1969 and remained at approximately 30 million hours. The limited growth in world-wide general aviation flying hours between 1969 and 1970 may be attributed in part to the limited growth of this type of flying in the United States, which accounts for over 80% of the total for the 119 ICAO contracting states. In other states there was a substantial increase in private aviation flying in 1970.

Hours flown in U.S. general aviation in 1959 totaled 12,903,000 and reached 25,351,000 in 1969, an increase of close to 100%. Only a slight increase in 1970 was recorded, primarily due to the slow down in the nation's economy. According to FAA, by late fiscal year 1971 the economy is expected to return to a more normal growth rate and the general aviation flying will show a corresponding recovery reaching 33,800,000 hours by fiscal year 1975, Speas figures (see Principal References, page 117) show a similar trend. *Figure 5* summarizes the information.

Figure 4

ACTIVE GENERAL AVIATION PILOTS
ACTUAL AND FORECAST

1959 – 1975

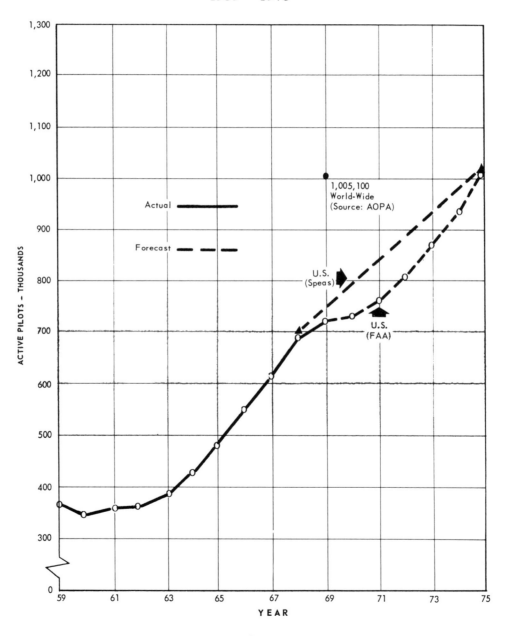

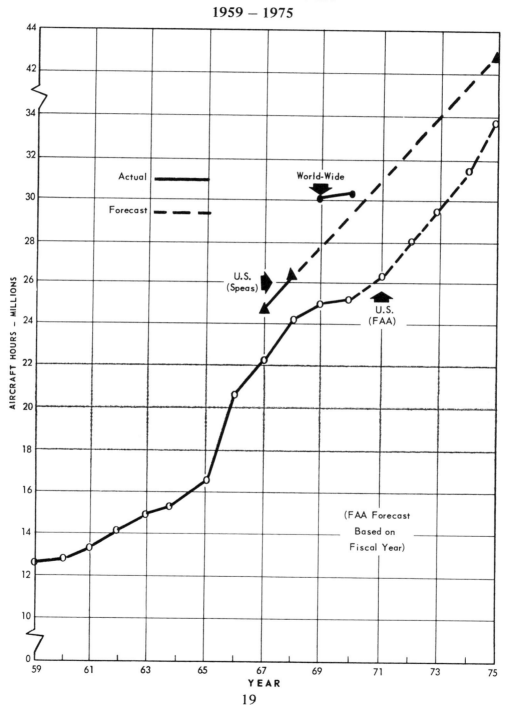

Figure 5
GENERAL AVIATION FLYING HOURS
ACTUAL AND FORECAST
1959 – 1975

6. ACCIDENT STATISTICS

An overall statistical review of the safety record of general aviation in the U.S. over the 11-year period 1959–1969 reveals that flying was much safer at the end of the period than at the beginning.

There was substantial improvement between 1959 and 1966 and, after remaining almost unchanged from 1966 through 1969, additional improvement in safety was shown in 1970. The total fatalities in 1970 were 1,270, down 15% from the 1969 total of 1,495 fatalities.

Since complete statistics for 1970 are not yet available, this phase does not extend beyond 1969. It should be borne in mind that the accident statistics which follow include all civil aircraft operation except those defined by NTSB as "air carrier operations authorized by a certificate of convenience and necessity issued by the CAB." Hence they encompass not only personal flying, business transport and air taxi but also aerial application such as crop dusting, industrial/special operation such as pipeline patrol, and training and experimental test flying. Using 1968 data, the contribution of these types of operations to the total accident picture is as follows:

Type of Flying	TOTAL ACCIDENTS		FATAL ACCIDENTS	
	Number	Rate*	Number	Rate*
Personal flying	2,291	30.93	384	5.17
Business transport	681	13.18	95	1.84
Other Non-commercial flying	148	32.88	11	2.44
Air Taxi	176	8.80	45	2.25
Aerial application	367	28.63	39	3.04
Other Commercial flying	106	11.05	18	1.87
Instructional flying	993	15.16	65	0.99
Experiment, test demonstration, air show, etc.	241	100.00	45	18.67
Overall rate		20.65		2.86

per 100,000 flying hours

Statistics relating to fatal accidents, fatalities, aircraft loss and the rates thereof, reveal that from 1966 through 1969 the fatal accident rate remained at about 2.7 per 100,000 aircraft hours or 0.175 per million aircraft miles; fatalities remained at about 5.55 per 100,000 aircraft hours or at 18 per 100 million passenger miles and the aircraft loss remained at 0.30 per million aircraft miles.

The fatality rate in general aviation, approximately 18 per 100 million passenger miles, is higher than in automobile travel which was 2.3 in 1969, according to the National Safety Council.[13]

---

[13]Accident Facts – 1970, NSC.

However, general aviation injures only one person for each two fatalities, 697 injuries in 1969, while the automobile injures 27 for each fatality, over 1,500,000 injuries in 1969. This aspect is discussed further under the subject of crashworthiness.

In its preliminary estimates on 1970 U.S. transportation fatalities, the NTSB shows the following:

Total Highway		53,830
Car drivers/occupants	41,120	
Pedestrians	9,900	
Motorcycle	1,960	
Bicycle	850	
Grade crossing		1,470
Marine (Recreational)		1,350
General aviation		1,270
Railroad		689
Marine (Commercial)		430
Air Carriers		146
Pipeline		35
Total Transportation		59,220

General aviation fatalities in 1970, therefore, fell between those of pleasure-boating and bicycling.

Detailed analysis of the accident statistics appear in Chapter 7 Accident Analysis beginning on page 32.

Definitions

In setting down statistics in any field a definition of terms is needed. The definitions for general aviation accident statistics are offered below. One factor which makes difficult a direct comparison of most of the accident "rate" values after 1967 with those of 1967 and earlier years comes from the change in definition of "substantial damage," made by the NTSB in January 1968.

The effect of the change which eased the definition of an accident by removing the specific $300 loss value and reduced the amount of reporting, was to decrease the total number of accidents reported each year, thereby changing the base for a number of tabulations. In the figures shown in this section of the report, the change is indicated by a discontinuity in curves between 1967 and 1968.

In the determination of rates in the following sections, the statistical values of accidents, fatalities and injuries from the NTSB are combined with FAA values on hours and miles flown.

The following definitions are taken from NTSB regulations Part 430 pertaining to accident investigation:

Aircraft Accident — An occurrence associated with the operation of an aircraft which takes place between the time any person boards aircraft with the intention of flight until such time as all such persons have disembarked, in which any person suffers death or serious injury as a result of being in or upon the aircraft or by direct contact with the aircraft or anything attached thereto, or the aircraft receives substantial damage.

Fatal Injury — Any injury which results in death within seven days.

Serious Injury — Any injury which (1) requires hospitalization for more than 48 hours, commencing within 7 days from the date the injury was received; (2) results in a fracture of any bone (except simple fracture of fingers, toes, or nose); (3) involves lacerations which cause severe hemorrhages, nerve, muscle or tendon damage; (4) involves injury to any internal organ; or (5) involves second or third degree burns, or any burns affecting more than 5 percent of the body surface.

Substantial Damage (Prior to January 1, 1968) — Substantial damage in aircraft of 12,500 pounds (5,670 kg) maximum certificated takeoff weight or less means damage or structural failure reasonably *estimated to cost $300 or more to repair.*

Substantial damage in aircraft of more than 12,500 pounds maximum certificated takeoff weight means damage or structural failure which adversely affects the structural strength, performance, or flight characteristics of the aircraft, and which normally would require major repairs or replacement of the affected component.

Engine failure, damage limited to an engine, bent fairings or cowling, dented skin, small punctured holes in the skin or fabric, taxiing damage to propeller blades, damage to tires, engine accessories, brakes or wingtips are not considered "substantial damage" for the purpose of this part.

However, changes also were made to the definition of "substantial damage" and, as described in the discussion which follows, this has had an effect on the statistical base. The revised definition, which no longer differentiates between aircraft more or less than 12,500 pounds weight, is:

Substantial Damage (Effective January 1, 1968) — Substantial damage means damage or structural failure which adversely affects the structural strength, performance, or flight characteristics of the aircraft, and which normally would *require major repair or replacement of the affected component.*

Discussion

Figures 6, 7, 8, 9, 10 and 11 which follow show accident statistics and rates for general aviation for the 11-year period 1959 thru 1969.

Number of Accidents — A statistical review of the safety record of general aviation over the past 11 years, as shown in *Figure 6,* reveals that the number of accidents increased from 4,576 in 1959 to 6,115 in 1967, and then dropped to 4,968 in 1968 and 4,767 in 1969. As compared with total number of accidents in 1967, the total number of accidents reported in 1968 declined about 20%. This decline may be primarily attributed to the effect of the change in the definition of "substantial damage" discussed earlier.

Accident and Fatality Rates — During the 11-year period, the number of fatal accidents and fatalities increased slightly while fatal accident rates and fatality rates fell moderately. The annual increase and decrease of accidents, fatal accidents and fatalities and rates are shown in *Figures 6, 7* and *8.*

Of particular interest are *Figures 7* and *8. Figure 7* shows that the fatal accident rate fell from 0.26 to 0.17 accidents per million aircraft miles (1,609,000 km) flown, and *Figure 8* shows that the fatality rate per 100 million passenger (and crew, in general aviation) miles flown reduced from 25 to 17. The latter values are still much higher than scheduled air carrier, rail or passenger automobile.

Figure 9 shows the fatalities and serious injuries as a percent of number of passengers and pilots aboard the aircraft involved in accidents. The fatality rate increased from 9.6 in 1962 to 10.9 in 1967, and jumped significantly in 1968 and 1969. As pointed out earlier, the big increase in rate from 1967 to 1968 is attributed primarily to the change in definition of an accident. Since the total number of reported accidents in 1968 decreased almost 20% from that in 1967, the total number of persons aboard the aircraft involved in accidents decreased accordingly; hence the rate of fatalities as a percent of total aboard is correspondingly higher. However, even if the fatality rates in 1968 and 1969 are adjusted by reducing them 20%, the rates are still 10.8% and 11.4% respectively.

In this connection, the most significant factor shown in *Figure 9* is that a rising trend in both fatalities and serious injuries prevailed over those years. It follows that although the chance of being involved in an aircraft accident has decreased over the past few years, the consequences to those who do become involved are more serious.

Aircraft Loss Rates: The number of aircraft involved in accidents and number of aircraft destroyed, and aircraft loss rates are shown in *Figures 10* and *11.* Over this period (1959-1969), the number of aircraft destroyed fluctuated in the neighborhood of one thousand units.

Measured by aircraft miles and hours, the aircraft loss rate was one aircraft lost per 1,456,000 aircraft miles or 10,953 hours in 1959 and 3,728,000 aircraft miles or 23,364 hours in 1969. The improvement is more than 100% which is very significant, i.e., there is twice as much use per accident. However, one aspect of data contained in *Figure 10* is not so encouraging. If a 20% reduction adjustment were made to the rates in 1968 and 1969 due to the change in the definition of accidents, over five consecutive years (1965-1969) the number of aircraft destroyed as a percent of total aircraft involved in accidents would still remain at the 18% level shown in *Figure 10.* In other words, in an accident there is one chance in five of the aircraft being destroyed.

Fire Involvement: It should be noted in *Figure 12* that during the years 1962-1969, the number of accidents involving fire increased from 211 in 1962 to 337 in 1969. The annual increase rate was 9%. During the first six years (1962-1967) and the last two years (1968-1969), fire was involved in an average of 5% and 7% of total general aviation accidents respectively. Moreover, over these 11 years, nearly 30% of all fatal accidents involved fire and an average of 60% of the accidents involving fire were fatal. It is significant that the rate of fatal accidents involving fire is increasing.

24

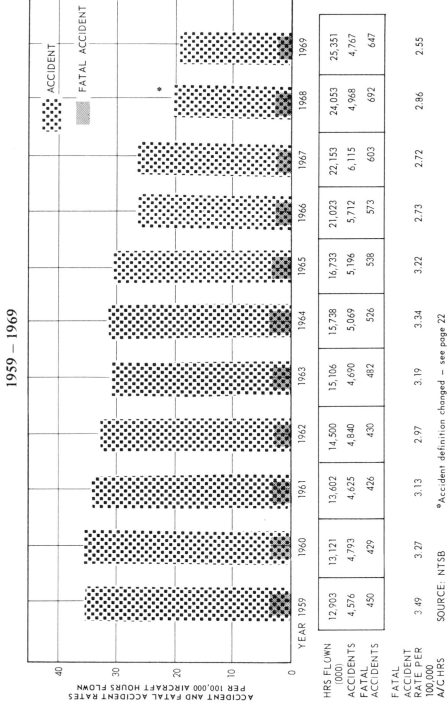

Figure 6

GENERAL AVIATION ACCIDENT AND FATAL ACCIDENT RATES
1959 – 1969

	YEAR 1959	1960	1961	1962	1963	1964	1965	1966	1967	1968	1969
HRS FLOWN (000)	12,903	13,121	13,602	14,500	15,106	15,738	16,733	21,023	22,153	24,053	25,351
ACCIDENTS	4,576	4,793	4,625	4,840	4,690	5,069	5,196	5,712	6,115	4,968	4,767
FATAL ACCIDENTS	450	429	426	430	482	526	538	573	603	692	647
FATAL ACCIDENT RATE PER 100,000 A/C HRS	3.49	3.27	3.13	2.97	3.19	3.34	3.22	2.73	2.72	2.86	2.55

SOURCE: NTSB

*Accident definition changed — see page 22

25

Figure 7

GENERAL AVIATION AIRCRAFT MILES FLOWN AND FATAL
ACCIDENT RATE PER MILLION AIRCRAFT MILES FLOWN

1959 – 1969

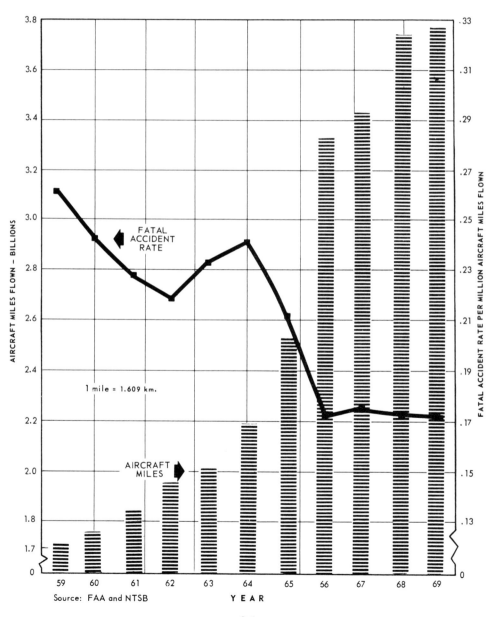

Source: FAA and NTSB

Figure 8

FATALITY RATE PER 100 MILLION PASSENGER-MILES
GENERAL AVIATION

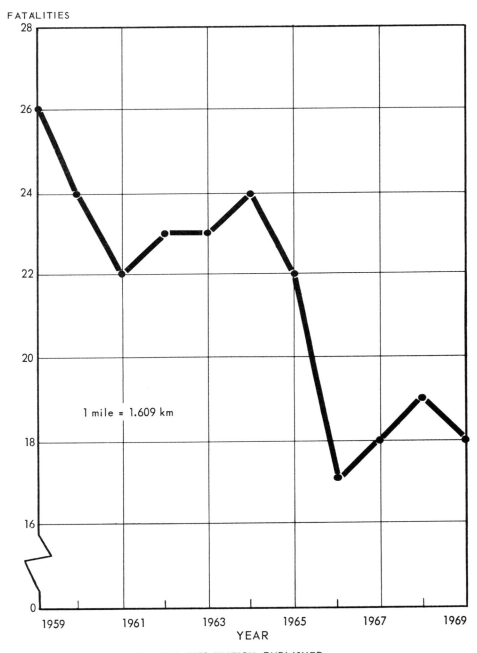

SOURCE: ACCIDENT FACTS, 1970 EDITION, PUBLISHED
BY NATIONAL SAFETY COUNCIL

27

Figure 9

FATALITIES AND SERIOUS INJURIES AS A
PERCENT OF TOTAL ABOARD
GENERAL AVIATION

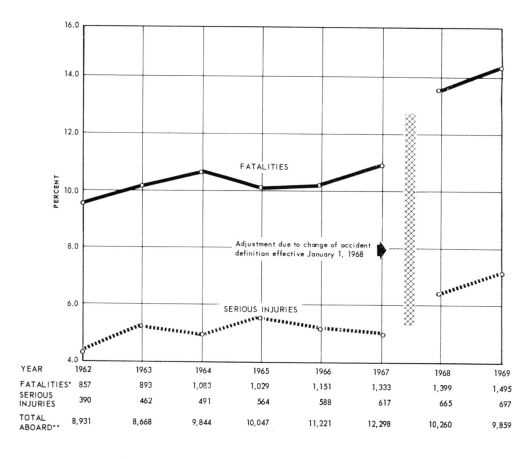

YEAR	1962	1963	1964	1965	1966	1967	1968	1969
FATALITIES*	857	893	1,083	1,029	1,151	1,333	1,399	1,495
SERIOUS INJURIES	390	462	491	564	588	617	665	697
TOTAL ABOARD**	8,931	8,668	9,844	10,047	11,221	12,298	10,260	9,859

*Occupants aboard air carrier and military aircraft when involved in collisions are included but excluded in computation of rate.

**Total number of passengers and crew members aboard the aircraft involved in accidents. Data prior to 1962 are not available.

Source: NTSB Annual Review of U.S. General Aviation, Annual Editions.

28

Figure 10

NUMBER OF AIRCRAFT DESTROYED AS A PERCENT OF TOTAL AIRCRAFT INVOLVED IN ACCIDENTS

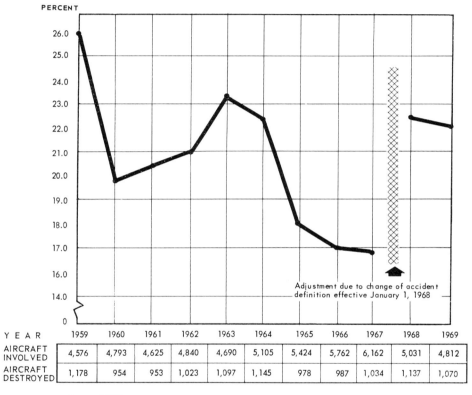

YEAR	1959	1960	1961	1962	1963	1964	1965	1966	1967	1968	1969
AIRCRAFT INVOLVED	4,576	4,793	4,625	4,840	4,690	5,105	5,424	5,762	6,162	5,031	4,812
AIRCRAFT DESTROYED	1,178	954	953	1,023	1,097	1,145	978	987	1,034	1,137	1,070

Source: NTSB

29

Figure 11

AIRCRAFT TOTAL-LOSS RATE
PER MILLION AIRCRAFT MILES AND
PER AIRCRAFT HOURS

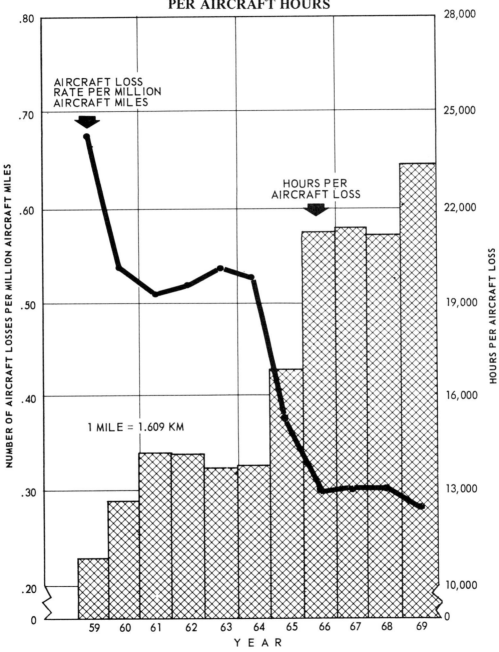

Source: Annual Review of General Aviation
Accidents 1959 through 1968

30

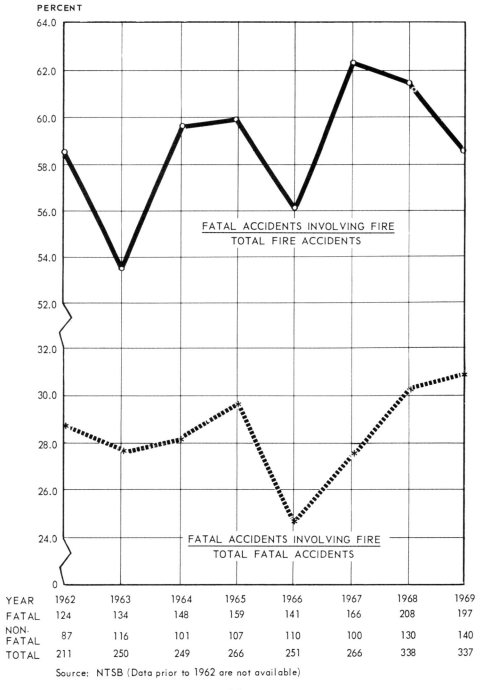

Figure 12
ACCIDENTS AND FATAL ACCIDENTS INVOLVING
FIRE AFTER IMPACT

PERCENT

FATAL ACCIDENTS INVOLVING FIRE
TOTAL FIRE ACCIDENTS

FATAL ACCIDENTS INVOLVING FIRE
TOTAL FATAL ACCIDENTS

YEAR	1962	1963	1964	1965	1966	1967	1968	1969
FATAL	124	134	148	159	141	166	208	197
NON-FATAL	87	116	101	107	110	100	130	140
TOTAL	211	250	249	266	251	266	338	337

Source: NTSB (Data prior to 1962 are not available)

$7._$ ACCIDENT ANALYSIS

In order to analyze the critical trends and patterns dealing with the safety of general aviation fixed-wing aircraft and to indicate avenues of promise for greater safety, a comprehensive study of the NTSB reports of general aviation accidents for the calendar years 1968 and 1969 has been made. The study has been limited to fixed-wing airplanes not exceeding 12,500 pound maximum takeoff weight, which constitute about 97% of the general aviation fleet. Typically, these airplanes meet the normal category rules of FAR 23. The remaining 3% include transport category airplanes (FAR 25), helicopters, seaplanes, gliders, etc.

Fire

As shown earlier under Fire Involvement, page 24 and in *Figure 12,* the occurance of fire in accidents has been increasing. As will be shown later in *Figure 18,* the fatality rate increases six-fold if there is fire following impact. Obviously, a portion of these fatalities would have resulted from the severity of the impact, whether there was fire or not. Study of specific accidents, however, show many cases of otherwise survivable accidents ending as fatal accidents because of fire. It is for these reasons that this analysis differs from most in that the primary break-down is "fire after impact" and "no fire after impact" rather than the usual phase-of-operation, type of accident, cause factor. However, the latter are covered in the analyses and discussions beginning on page 34.

Number of Engines and Wing Location

Designation as single- or multi-engine aircraft is done routinely in NTSB records but designation or classification by wing location is not. For the latter purpose, use was made of information available from the study made by NTSB on the effect of some design features of aircraft in inducing errors by pilots to[14], and the listings of high-and low-wing airplane types were developed from this.

Summaries

The method of analysis is shown in *Figure 13.* Summaries of phase-of-operation, type of accident and cause/factor are covered on pages 34 through 37; summaries for single- and multi-engine airplanes are shown on page 51; high- versus low-wing airplanes on page 59, and the findings on page 60. Review of some selected accidents appears on pages 78 through 107.

---

[14]Aircraft Design-Induced Pilot Error. NTSB Report No. 175 629, July 1967.

Figure 13

SCHEMATIC DIAGRAM – METHODS OF ANALYSIS

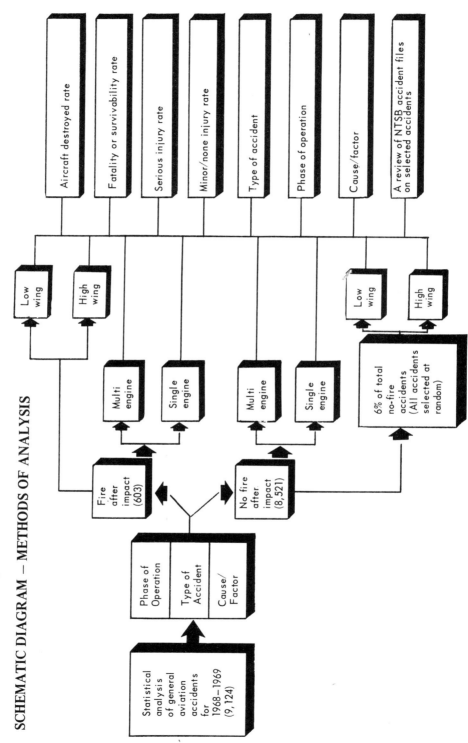

Phase of Operation

An annual breakdown of general aviation accidents by phase of operation for the years 1968 and 1969 is shown in *Figure 14.* Approach and landing accidents account for 48% and 51% respectively of the total accidents. In-flight accidents account for 25%–27%, takeoff and initial climb accounted for 17%–19%, and taxi accidents for 4% of total accidents. Over this period, no phase of operation showed any significant increase or decrease in frequency.

Figure 14.

PHASE OF OPERATION

Phase	1968		1969	
	Number	Percent	Number	Percent
STATIC	30	.6	28	.6
TAXI	199	4.3	165	3.7
TAKEOFF – INITIAL CLIMB	812	17.4	844	18.9
IN-FLIGHT	1,179	25.3	1,215	27.3
APPROACH-LANDING	2,380	51.0	2,152	48.3
UNDETER-MINED	65	1.4	55	1.2
TOTALS	4,665	100.0	4,459	100.0

Type of Accident

Type of accident relates to the immediate circumstances of the occurrence. Many accidents involve a series of circumstances. Of the 57 different accident-types defined by the National Transportation Safety Board,

34

the following "first accident types" listed collectively, account for 80% of all fatal accidents, 71% of all accidents wherein the aircraft involved were totally destroyed, and some 70% of serious injury accidents for the year 1967:[15]

a. Stall/spin/mush,
b. Collision with ground/water,
c. Collision with wire/poles/trees/other objects,
d. Engine failure or malfunction.

The frequency of the accident-types mentioned above occurring in accidents involving fire after impact is even higher. Of the 603 small fixed-wing aircraft accidents involving fire after impact for the years 1968 and 1969, 502 accidents, or over 83% occurred in the above-mentioned circumstances. A detailed breakdown is shown in *Figure 15.*

Mid-air collision, a problem of increasing concern, contributes only a small percentage to the accident totals. Over the ten-year period 1961-1970 inclusive, for all types of civil operations they average 25 accidents per year. Collisions involving air carriers totaled 11 for an average of 1.1 per year.

Cause/Factor

The principal breakdown of the causes and related factors of all accidents for the years 1968 and 1969 is shown in *Figure 16.* It should be noted that for statistical purposes, where two or more causes exist in an accident, each is recorded. Therefore, in the figure showing the cause and related factor, total percentage will exceed 100%.

The pilot was cited most frequently as a cause of accidents while weather, mechanical and terrain were cited most often as related factors. Of all mechanical accidents, powerplant and landing gear were cited more frequently as a cause of accidents than other mechanical failures.

Personnel other than the pilot were involved in 8% of all accidents. Such personnel include flight instructor, maintenance, servicing, inspection, operational supervisory personnel, weather, air traffic control, airport, and airway supervisory personnel.

Additional discussion of cause/factor as related to single-engine versus multi-engine types of aircraft will be found on page 41.

---

[15]National Transportation Safety Board, An Analysis of Aircraft Accident Data, U.S. General Aviation, 1967.

Figure 15

TYPE OF ACCIDENT

Fire After Impact

First Type Accidents	1968		1969		Two Year Totals	
	Fatal	Non-Fatal	Fatal	Non-Fatal	Total	Percent
Stall/Spin	58	23	48	26	155	25.7%
Collision with Poles/Trees/Other	33	26	42	24	125	20.7%
Collision with Ground/Water	55	7	53	7	122	20.2%
Engine Failure/ Malfunction	22	27	18	33	100	16.6%
Undershoot/ Overshoot	2	12	3	3	20	3.3%
Mid-Air Collision	10	0	2	1	13	2.1%
Gear up/Re- tracted	0	3	0	9	12	2.0%
Hard Landing	0	6	0	4	10	1.7%
Ground-Water Loop	1	5	1	3	10	1.7%
Airframe Failure	5	1	1	1	8	1.3%
Gear Collapse	0	4	0	3	7	1.2%
Turbulence	2	2	2	1	7	1.2%
Miscellaneous/ Undetermined	6	2	6	0	14	2.3%
TOTALS	194	118	176	115	603	100.0%

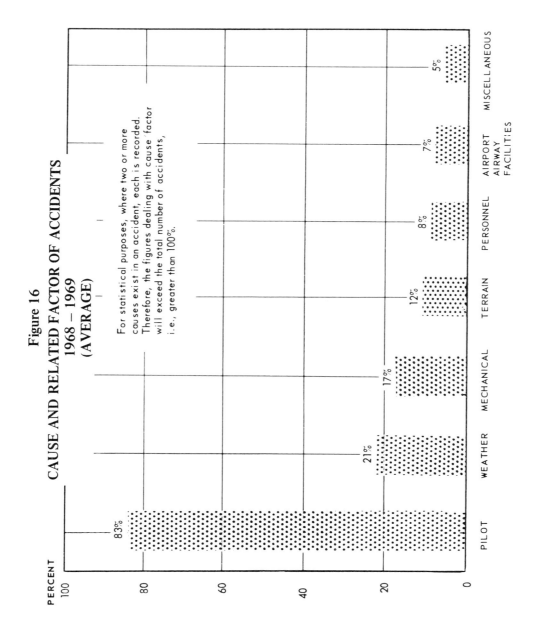

Figure 16
CAUSE AND RELATED FACTOR OF ACCIDENTS
1968 – 1969
(AVERAGE)

For statistical purposes, where two or more causes exist in an accident, each is recorded. Therefore, the figures dealing with cause factor will exceed the total number of accidents, i.e., greater than 100%.

Fire Involvement and Survivability

During the two-year period (1968-1969), a total of 9,124 small fixed-wing aircraft accidents was recorded. Of these, 603, or 6.6% of the total, involved fire after impact. A comparison of accidents with and without fire involvement is shown in *Figure 17.*

Of the accidents involving fire, over 61% were fatal accidents against only 10.6% of the accidents in which no fire was involved. In terms of aircraft damage, 93% of the aircraft involving fire were totally destroyed, the remaining 7% were recorded as having sustained substantial damage. If fire did not occur, only 17.7% of the aircraft were totally destroyed.

Figure 18 shows the injury index relating to fire involvement. Of the total persons aboard the aircraft in accidents involving fire, 62% were killed; of the persons aboard the aircraft in accidents without fire involvement, only 10.6% were killed. The statistics definitely show that if fire did not occur the chance of survival for the occupants aboard the aircraft was much greater. No doubt some of the fatalities in fire involvement accidents resulted from the impact itself, which also caused fuel spillage and subsequent fire. However, many accidents occur at relatively low impact-velocity and a non-fatal type of accident may become fatal because of impact fire. This phase is examined in some detail beginning on page 104.

Current NTSB reports generally do not provide information as to whether fatalities in cases of fire after impact were due to the impact or to the fire. In some cases the narrative sections of the report contains the information, and autopsies, where conducted and when available, do provide the information. More specific information on this phase would assist in the development of improved safety standards.

Although increased efforts to reduce the crash fire hazard have been made, it remains one of the critical problems in flight safety.

Figure 17

ACCIDENTS AND AIRCRAFT DAMAGE

FIRE vs NO FIRE

1968 – 1969

	FIRE AFTER IMPACT		NO FIRE AFTER IMPACT	
	Number	Percent of Total	Number	Percent of Total
Total Accidents	603	100.0	8,521	100.0
Accidents involving Fatalities	370	61.4	901	10.6
Accidents involving Serious Injuries	82	13.6	597	7.0
Accidents involving Minor Injuries	64	10.6	1,121	13.2
Accidents without Injuries	87	14.4	5,902	69.2
Total Aircraft Involved	618	100.0	8,613	100.0
Aircraft destroyed	575	93.0	1,525	17.7
Substantial Damage	43	7.0	7,024	81.6
Minor/None	—	0.	64	0.7

Figure 18
INJURY INDEX FIRE VS. NO FIRE
1968 – 1969

	FIRE AFTER IMPACT		NO FIRE AFTER IMPACT	
	Number	Percent	Number	Percent
Total Aboard	1,364	100.0	17,412	100.0
Fatal Injuries	847	62.1	1,842	10.6
Serious Injuries	167	12.2	1,085	6.2
Minor Injuries	148	10.9	1,886	10.8
None	202	14.8	12,599	72.4

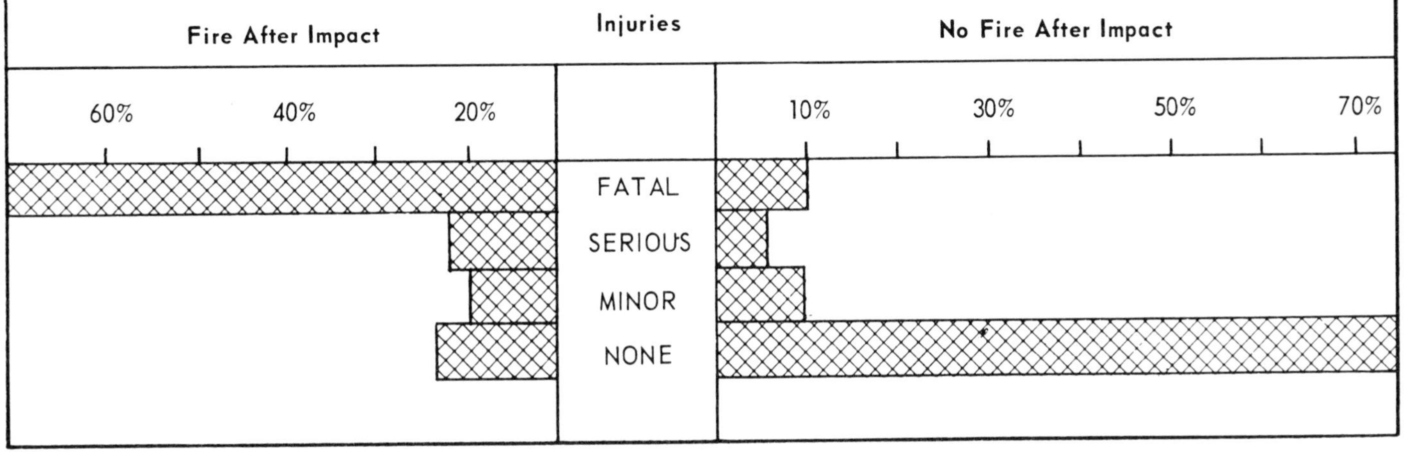

Fire After Impact

Injuries

No Fire After Impact

FATAL
SERIOUS
MINOR
NONE

60% 40% 20% 10% 30% 50% 70%

Single-Engine vs. Multi-Engine Aircraft

Of all small fixed-wing active aircraft registered in 1968 and 1969, single-engine aircraft account for about 87.5% of the total, and multi-engine aircraft account for the remaining 12.5%. The average total annual flying time during the two-year period was 19.5 million hours per year for single-engine aircraft and 4.1 million hours for multi-engine aircraft. In other words, the average single-engine aircraft flew 183 hours per year while the multi-engine aircraft flew 270 hours per year. The total number of accidents to single-engine aircraft as a percentage of the total number of single-engine aircraft is higher than the percentage for multi-engine aircraft, i.e., 3.84% against 3.13%. However, fatal accidents as a percentage of total accidents average 13% for single-engine and 20% for multi-engine aircraft.

Multi-engine aircraft fly more hours per year than single-engine aircraft, and when involved in an accident the consequences are more serious.

The latter may result from one or more of the following:

a.   Multi-engine aircraft have higher takeoff and landing speeds than single-engine aircraft,

b.   Carry larger amounts of fuel,

c.   Are used more in IFR operation, and weather accidents typically are more severe than other types.

To verify statement *a,* (above), regarding speeds, a brief separate study was made.

The five most numerous type general aviation single-engine airplanes and the five most numerous type multi-engine airplanes were taken from the 1969 FAA Census of U.S. Aircraft and the corresponding maximum wing loadings of each were taken from Jane's All the World's Aircraft. The weighted average wing loadings were found to be:

Single-Engine (41,350 airplanes) — 13.6 psf (66.5 kg/m^2)

Multi-Engine (8,326 airplanes) — 28.0 psf (137 kg/m^2)

The wing loading of multi-engine airplanes is just over twice that of the single-engine types. If it is assumed that the airfoil and flap combinations of both single-engine and multi-engine airplanes can develop the same maximum lift per unit of area, i.e., the same maximum lift coefficient, then the multi-engine aircraft on the average will land at a speed some 40% higher than the single-engine airplane, and with double the kinetic energy per unit weight to be dissipated. However, some gain in crashworthiness will come from the larger dimensions and greater mass of the twin.

Aircraft Destroyed. Of the accidents, including both fire after impact or no fire after impact wherein the aircraft involved were destroyed, more than 50% were fatal. *Figure 19* shows the fatal accidents, fatalities, and corresponding rates of single-engine against multi-engine aircraft. The statistics showed that fire involvement resulted in not only more serious damage to aircraft but also a higher number of fatal injuries. However, the damage and fatal injury index involving multi-engine aircraft is slightly higher than that relating to single-engine aircraft. As to fatality rate (i.e., occupants) per 100,000 flying hours, it is 6.2 for multi-engine aircraft and 5.3 for single-engine aircraft, the former almost 20% higher than the latter. This higher fatality rate in multi-engine aircraft may be attributed, among other things, to the fact that typically a multi-engine aircraft carries about 30% more persons than a single-engine aircraft. One other difference in accident rate between these two types of aircraft is that if no fire was involved, fatal accidents as a percent of total accidents are 52.6% in single-engine aircraft against 72.2% for multi-engine aircraft.

Aircraft Receiving Substantial Damage. An analysis of survivability in the accident wherein the aircraft involved received substantial damage is shown in *Figure 20.* Of the accidents involving fire, the figures are too small to make a meaningful comparison. Of the accidents involving no fire, just over one percent of the total accidents were fatal in both single-engine and multi-engine aircraft. These statistics may indicate the benefit of fuel containment under impact, or that severe impact is more likely to result in fire.

Cause or Factor. Tabulations of the cause or factor in accidents based on whether there was fire or not following impact and whether the aircraft was destroyed or not appear in *Figures 21* through *24.*

Summary. An overall summation of the single and multi-engine data is shown in *Figure 25.*

42

Figure 19

SMALL FIXED-WING AIRCRAFT ACCIDENTS
WHEREIN THE AIRCRAFT INVOLVED WERE DESTROYED
INJURY RATE
Single-Engine Aircraft
vs
Multi-Engine Aircraft
1968 – 1969 Average

FIRE AFTER IMPACT **(AIRCRAFT DESTROYED)**	Single- Engine	Multi- Engine	Total
Accidents	228	53	281
Fatal Accidents	149	36	185
Fatal Accidents as a Percent of Total Accidents	65.4%	67.9%	65.8%
Total Aboard Aircraft	417	179	596
Fatal Injuries	301	118	419
Serious Injuries	52	27	79
Minor/No Injuries	64	34	98
Fatal Injuries as a Percent of Total Aboard	72.2%	65.9%	70.3%
Serious Injuries as a Percent of Total Aboard	12.5%	15.1%	13.3%

NO FIRE AFTER IMPACT **(AIRCRAFT DESTROYED)**			
Accidents	658	77	735
Fatal Accidents	346	56	402
Fatal Accidents as a Percent of Total Accidents	52.6%	72.7%	54.7%
Total Aboard Aircraft	1,468	221	1,689
Fatal Injuries	727	137	864
Serious Injuries	253	41	294
Minor/No Injuries	488	43	531
Fatal Injuries as a Percent of Total Aboard	49.5%	61.9%	51.2%
Serious Injuries as a Percent of Total Aboard	17.2%	18.5%	17.4%

TOTAL FIRE AND NO-FIRE			
Fatality Rate per 100,000 Flying Hours	5.3	6.2	5.4

43

Figure 20

SMALL FIXED-WING AIRCRAFT ACCIDENTS
WHEREIN THE AIRCRAFT INVOLVED RECEIVED SUBSTANTIAL DAMAGE

Single-Engine Aircraft
vs
Multi-Engine Aircraft

1968 – 1969 Average

FIRE AFTER IMPACT (AIRCRAFT DAMAGED)

	Single-Engine	Multi-Engine	Total
Total Accidents	15	6	21
Fatal Accidents	1	0	1
Fatalities	1	0	1

NO FIRE AFTER IMPACT (AIRCRAFT DAMAGED)

	Single-Engine	Multi-Engine	Total
Total Accidents	3,158	337	3,495
Fatal Accidents	38	4	42
Fatalities	94	9	103

TOTAL FIRE AND NO FIRE

	Single-Engine	Multi-Engine	Total
Total accidents	3,173	343	3,516
Fatal accidents	39	4	43
Fatalities	95	9	104
Fatal accidents as a percent of total accidents	1.23%	1.17%	1.22%

Cause or Factor — A breakdown of cause/factor by the following categories is shown in *Figures 21, 22, 23,* and *24:*

I   Fire after impact — aircraft involved were destroyed *(Figure 21);*

II   No fire after impact — aircraft involved were destroyed *(Figure 22);*

III   Fire after impact — aircraft involved received substantial damage *(Figure 23);*

IV   No fire after impact — Aircraft involved received substantial damage *(Figure 24).*

In the accidents of Category I, the pilot was cited as the cause/factor in 87% of total accidents in both single-engine and multi-engine aircraft as compared to 82% of single-engine and 75% of multi-engine aircraft in the accidents of Category II. In both cases, powerplant and weather were cited more often in multi-engine aircraft accidents than in single-engine aircraft accidents — around 70% and 40%, respectively. Of the accidents in Category III, pilot was cited in only 70% of single-engine aircraft accidents and 76% of multi-engine aircraft accidents as compared to 85% of single-engine aircraft and 68% of multi-engine aircraft accidents in Category IV.

It is interesting to note that a further analysis of pilot-involvement reveals that of the fatal and non-fatal accidents in all four categories, five types of pilot involvement were cited more often. In terms of frequency, they are:

Pilot-Involvement All Fatal Accidents	ORDER OF FREQUENCY	
	Single-Engine	Multi-Engine
Failed to obtain/maintain flying-speed	1	1
Continued VFR into adverse weather	2	2
Inadequate preflight preparation and planning	3	3
Improper IFR operations	—	4
Spatial disorientation	4	5
Attempted operation beyond experience/ability	5	—

| Pilot-Involvement | ORDER OF FREQUENCY | |
All Non-Fatal Accidents	Single-Engine	Multi-Engine
Failed to obtain/maintain flying-speed	1	4
Inadequate preflight preparation and planning	2	1
Improper level-off	3	2
Mismanagement of landing gear system	–	5
Failed to maintain directional control	4	–
Misjudged distance/speed	5	3

As to weather involvement, there exists a different pattern between accidents in different categories. In order of frequency, the three types of weather involvements cited most in Categories I and II (aircraft destroyed) accidents, were: (1) low ceiling; (2) fog; (3) rain. Of the accidents in Categories III and IV (aircraft damaged) the three types of weather involvement cited were: (1) unfavorable wind conditions; (2) conditions conducive to carburetor/induction system icing; (3) low ceiling.

The powerplant was cited frequently as a cause in accidents of all categories. This includes pilot-involvement causes such as running out of fuel and/or switching to empty tanks. One of the causes relating to powerplant failure which was cited most often is, "Powerplant failure for undetermined reason."

As might be expected, landing gear is cited more often in accidents of Categories III and IV — aircraft damaged — than in accidents of Categories I and II. The most troublesome areas in landing gear systems are: (1) braking system; (2) normal retraction and extension assembly; and (3) gear lock mechanism.

Figure 21

CAUSE/FACTOR
FIRE AFTER IMPACT
AIRCRAFT INVOLVED WERE DESTROYED

Single-Engine Aircraft vs Multi-Engine Aircraft

1968 — 1969

Cause/Factor	SINGLE-ENGINE		MULTI-ENGINE	
	Accidents	Percent of Total	Accidents	Percent of Total
Pilot	398	87.47	91	86.67
Personnel	25	5.49	7	6.67
Airframe	6	1.32	1	.95
Landing gear	4	.88	—	—
Powerplant	40	8.79	15	14.29
System	2	.44	1	.95
Instrument/Equipment and Accessories	2	.44	4	3.81
Airport/Airways/ Facilities	14	3.08	2	1.90
Weather	122	26.81	40	38.10
Terrain	38	8.35	5	4.76
Miscellaneous	13	2.85	4	3.81
Undetermined	26	5.71	5	4.76

NOTE: The above tabulation is based upon 455 single-engine accidents and 105 multi-engine accidents. The totals shown exceed these values since, for statistical purposes, where two or more causes exist for an accident each is recorded.

Figure 22

CAUSE/FACTOR
NO FIRE AFTER IMPACT
AIRCRAFT INVOLVED WERE DESTROYED

Single-Engine Aircraft vs Multi-Engine Aircraft
1968 – 1969

Cause/Factor	SINGLE-ENGINE		MULTI-ENGINE	
	Accidents	Percent of Total	Accidents	Percent of Total
Pilot	1,086	82.46	117	76.47
Personnel	112	8.50	13	8.50
Airframe	26	1.97	1	.65
Landing gear	4	.30	—	—
Powerplant	129	9.79	27	17.65
Systems	7	.53	2	1.31
Instruments/ Equipment and Accessories	8	.61	3	1.96
Airport/Airways/ Facilities	28	2.13	1	.65
Weather	380	28.85	64	41.84
Terrain	121	9.19	10	6.54
Miscellaneous	46	3.49	3	1.96
Undetermined	94	7.14	19	12.42

NOTE: The above tabulation is based upon 1,317 single-engine accidents and 153 multi-engine accidents. The totals shown exceed these values since, for statistical purposes, where two or more causes exist for an accident each is recorded.

Figure 23

CAUSE/FACTOR

FIRE AFTER IMPACT

AIRCRAFT INVOLVED RECEIVED SUBSTANTIAL DAMAGE

Single-Engine Aircraft vs Multi-Engine Aircraft
1968 – 1969

Cause/Factor	SINGLE-ENGINE		MULTI-ENGINE	
	Accidents	Percent of Total	Accidents	Percent of Total
Pilot	21	70.00	10	76.92
Personnel	3	10.00	—	—
Airframe	—	—	—	—
Landing gear	1	3.33	2	15.38
Powerplant	4	13.33	3	23.08
System	1	3.33	—	—
Instrument/Equipment and Accessories	—	—	—	—
Airport/Airways/ Facilities	3	10.00	—	—
Weather	8	26.67	1	7.69
Terrain	5	16.67	—	—
Miscellaneous	1	3.33	—	—
Undetermined	1	3.33	—	—

NOTE: The above tabulation is based upon 30 single-engine accidents and 13 multi-engine accidents. The totals shown exceed these values since, for statistical purposes, where two or more causes exist for an accident each is recorded.

Figure 24

CAUSE/FACTOR
NO FIRE AFTER IMPACT
AIRCRAFT INVOLVED RECEIVED SUBSTANTIAL DAMAGE

Single-Engine Aircraft vs Multi-Engine Aircraft

1968 – 1969

Cause/Factor	SINGLE-ENGINE		MULTI-ENGINE	
	Accidents Accidents	Percent of Total	Accidents	Percent of Total
Pilot	5,378	85.15	459	68.20
Personnel	471	7.46	89	13.22
Airframe	35	.55	8	1.19
Landing gear	316	5.00	153	22.73
Powerplant	627	9.93	56	8.32
System	50	.79	10	1.49
Instruments/Equipment and Accessories	11	.17	3	.45
Airports/Airways/ Facilities	567	8.98	64	9.51
Weather	1,236	19.57	71	10.55
Terrain	877	13.89	24	3.57
Miscellaneous	179	2.83	20	2.97
Undetermined	32	.51	28	4.16

NOTE: The above tabulation is based upon 6,316 single-engine accidents and 673 multi-engine accidents. The totals shown exceed these values since, for statistical purposes, where two or more causes exist for an accident each is recorded.

Figure 25

S U M M A R Y

ACCIDENTS, FATAL ACCIDENTS
AND RATES
Single-Engine vs. Multi-Engine
1968 – 1969
(Average)

	SINGLE-ENGINE		MULTI-ENGINE	
	Total Accidents	Fatal Accidents	Total Accidents	Fatal Accidents
FIRE AFTER IMPACT				
Aircraft Damage:				
— Destroyed	228	149	53	36
— Substantial	15	1	6	0
— Minor/None	0	0	0	0
SUB-TOTALS	243	150	59	36
NO FIRE AFTER IMPACT				
Aircraft Damage:				
— Destroyed	658	346	77	56
— Substantial	3,158	38	337	4
— Minor/None	27	5	3	1
SUB-TOTALS	3,843	389	417	61
TOTAL, FIRE & NO-FIRE	4,086	539	476	97
Fatal accidents as a percent of total accidents	13.19		20.37	
Total active aircraft	106,255		15,230	
Aircraft involved in accidents as a percent of total aircraft	3.84	0.50	3.13	0.63
Total hours flown	19,500,000		4,100,000	
Rate per 100,000 hours	20.95	2.76	11.60	2.36

51

Low Wing vs. High-Wing Aircraft

An analysis of the accident pattern relating to high-wing and low-wing aircraft is another aspect of this study. Since NTSB accident statistics are not set up to readily provide information based on high-wing or low-wing configurations, the following listed high-wing and low-wing airplanes were used in this study. These are aircraft under 12,500 pounds gross weight, and there are more than 100 active aircraft for each of the specific models shown. Each of these models was involved in two or more accidents during the years 1968 and 1969:

High-Wing Aircraft

Aero Commander	Aeronca 11	Aeronca 65
Aeronca 15	Cessna 120	Cessna 140
Cessna 150	Cessna 170	Cessna 172
Cessna 175	Cessna 177	Cessna 180
Cessna 182	Cessna 185	
Cessna 195	Cessna 205	Cessna 206
Cessna 210	Cessna 337	Champion
Maule BD	Luscombe 8	Piper J-3/4/5
Piper PA-11	Piper PA-12	Piper PA-16
Piper PA-18	Piper PA-20	Piper PA-22
Stinson 108	Taylorcraft	

Low-Wing Aircraft

Alon A-2	American Yankee	Beech 18
Beech 23	Beech 33	Beech T-34
Beech 35	Beech 50	Beech 65
Beech 36	Beech 55	
Bellanca	Beech 95	Beech 95-55
Cessna 188	Callair A	Cessna 320
Cessna 310	Cessna 411	Cessna 421
Forney	Globe GC-1	Mooney M20
Navion	N. American AT-6	Piper PA-24
Piper PA-25	Piper PA-26	Piper PA-28
Piper PA-23	Piper PA-30	Piper PA-31

Based on the information contained in the FAA "Census of U.S. Civil Aircraft, as of December 31, 1969," it is estimated that the listed aircraft types totaled 114,900, about 59.8% of which were high-wing, 40.2% low-wing; about 87.5% of which were single-engine and 12.5% multi-engine. The distribution may be summarized as:

High-wing	single-engine — 58.1%
High-wing	multi-engine — 1.7%
Low-wing	single-engine — 29.5%
Low-wing	multi-engine — 10.7%

Note that while single-engine airplanes are well distributed between high- and low-wing types, the multi-engine airplanes are predominantly low-wing, i.e., 10.7% against 1.7%. Hence, about 6 out of 7 multi-engine general aviation airplanes are low-wing.

Fire after impact. Of 603 accidents involving fire, 229 were associated with high-wing aircraft, 339 were associated with low-wing aircraft, the remaining 35 were associated with either biplane or mid-wing types. A breakdown of accidents and fatalities by high- and low-wing types of aircraft is shown in *Figure 26.* Fatal accidents as a percent of total accidents were 64.2% for high-wing against 60.8% for low-wing. Aircraft destroyed as a percent of total aircraft involved were 93.5% for high-wing and 92.4% for low-wing aircraft. Survivors as a percent of total aboard were 34.6% in high-wing against 35.8% in low-wing aircraft. All of the rates for both types of aircraft are almost identical.

No fire after impact. Out of 8,521 accidents wherein there was no fire after impact, a total of 551 accidents were selected at random for detailed study. Three hundred and twelve of these involved high-wing, 210 involved low-wing aircraft, and the remaining 29 accidents were associated with either biplane or mid-wing aircraft. *Figure 27* shows a comparison of accident rates, aircraft destroyed rates and fatality rates between high-wing and low-wing aircraft. In terms of fatal accidents as a percent of total accidents, high-wing aircraft recorded 12.4% while low-wing recorded 14.5%. In terms of survivability, 88.1% of total aboard high-wing aircraft survived accidents while 86.9% of total aboard low-wing aircraft survived. Again, all of the rates for both types of aircraft were almost identical.

Phase-of-operation. A breakdown of accidents of the two types of aircraft by phase of operation is shown in *Figures 28* and *29.* Of the accidents involving fire, *Figure 28* shows that 48.5% of high-wing aircraft accidents against 37.2% of low-wing aircraft accidents occurred in flight, 21.8% of high-wing against 23.6% of low-wing occurred during approach and landing. In takeoff accidents, it was 21.4% for high-wing against 26.2% for low-wing. In a word, more high-wing aircraft accidents occurred in flight while more low-wing aircraft accidents occurred during landing and takeoff. Of the accidents with no fire involvement, *Figure 29* shows that approach and landing accounted for more than 54% of either high-wing or low-wing aircraft accidents. In takeoff accidents, high-wing aircraft accounted for 23% as compared with 20% for low-wing. Of the in-flight accidents, it was 18% for high-wing as compared with 22% for low-wing. Therefore, in terms of phase of operation there is no consistent accident pattern between high-wing and low-wing aircraft.

Relative involvement in fire. The statistics show that more low-wing than high-wing aircraft were involved in fire after impact. As indicated earlier, of the total active general aviation high-wing and low-wing aircraft, 60% were high-wing and 40% low-wing. Of 568 high-wing and low-wing aircraft accidents involving fire, *(Figure 26)* 339 or 60% involved low-wing against 229 involving high-wing.

The detailed breakdown follows:

Fire after impact

High-wing	Single-engine	221 (38.9%)
High-wing	Multi-engine	8 (1.4%)
Low-wing	Single-engine	233 (41.0%)
Low-wing	Multi-engine	106 (18.7%)

On a proportionate basis, the low-wing aircraft should have been involved in only 40% or 227 of the total of 568 accidents, and the high-wing aircraft should have been involved in 60% or 341 or the total accidents. However, the study reveals that the low-wing did incur 339 or 60% of the accidents involving fire while the high-wing aircraft were involved in 229 or 40% of the accidents involving fire.

As shown in *Figure 27,* the sample study of 522 no-fire accidents reveals that high-wing aircraft were involved in 312 or 60% and low-wing were involved in 210 or 40% of the accidents. The percentage of high-wing and low-wing aircraft involved in accidents of the no-fire category are in proportion to the total aircraft population.

In terms of fire involvement, however, the low-wing rate is almost 50% higher than the average rate for both high-wing and low-wing aircraft. Hence the low-wing airplane shows up as being more susceptible to fire after impact. Since six out of seven multi-engine airplanes are low-wing, it is possible that some of the reasons cited on page 41, such as higher contact speeds, greater amounts of fuel and more IFR operation, regarding the comparative seriousness of multi-engine aircraft accidents apply to low-wing aircraft as well.

General. Differences exist between high-wing and low-wing airplanes with respect to visibility in turns, and in their characteristics in ditching. Fortunately, the rarity of in-flight collision and ditching cases makes it difficult to establish a statistical basis to compare these aspects.

Figure 26

SMALL FIXED-WING AIRCRAFT ACCIDENTS*

FIRE AFTER IMPACT

High-Wing Aircraft

vs

Low-Wing Aircraft

1968 – 1969

	HIGH-WING	LOW-WING
Total Accidents	229	339
Fatal Accidents	147	206
Fatal Accidents as a Percent of Total Accidents	64.2%	60.8%
Total Aircraft Involved	232	341
Aircraft Destroyed	217	315
Aircraft Destroyed as a Percent of Total Aircraft Involved	93.5%	92.4%
Total Aboard	486	799
Fatalities	318	513
Serious Injuries	34	110
Minor/None	134	176
Survivors as a Percent Of Total Aboard	34.6%	35.8%

*Based on an analysis of 568 of a total of 603 fire accidents, the remaining 35 being associated with either biplane or mid-wing type airplanes.

55

Figure 27

SMALL FIXED-WING AIRCRAFT ACCIDENTS*

NO FIRE AFTER IMPACT

High-Wing Aircraft
vs.
Low-Wing Aircraft

1968 – 1969

	HIGH-WING	LOW-WING
Total Accidents	312	210
Fatal Accidents	38	30
Fatal Accidents as a Percent of Total Accidents	12.2%	14.3%
Total Aircraft Involved	314	215
Aircraft Destroyed	67	51
Aircraft Destroyed as a Percent of Total Aricraft Involved	21.3%	23.7%
Total Aboard	605	465
Fatalities	72	61
Serious Injuries	55	42
Minor/none	478	362
Survivors as a Percent of Total Aboard	88.1%	86.9%

*Based on an analysis of 522 accidents selected at random, of a total of 8,521 accidents.

Figure 28

SMALL FIXED-WING AIRCRAFT ACCIDENTS

PHASE-OF-OPERATION

High-Wing Aircraft vs. Low-Wing Aircraft

1968 – 1969

FIRE AFTER IMPACT

PHASE OF OPERATION	HIGH-WING		LOW-WING	
	Number of Accidents	Percent	Number of Accidents	Percent
Takeoff run — initial climb	49	21.4	89	26.2
In-flight — cruise and other	111	48.5	126	37.2
Descent	15	6.6	34	10.0
Approach & Landing	50	21.8	80	23.6
Taxiing	0	—	2	0.6
Undetermined	4	1.7	8	2.4
TOTAL	229	100.0	339	100.0

Figure 29

SMALL FIXED-WING AIRCRAFT ACCIDENTS

PHASE-OF-OPERATION

High-Wing Aircraft vs. Low-Wing Aircraft

1968 – 1969

NO FIRE AFTER IMPACT

PHASE OF OPERATION	HIGH-WING		LOW-WING	
	Number of Accidents	Percent	Number of Accidents	Percent
Takeoff run – initial climb	74	23.7	42	20.0
In-flight – cruise and other	55	17.6	46	21.9
Descent	3	1.0	4	1.9
Approach & Landing	172	55.1	115	54.8
Taxiing	5	1.6	3	1.4
Static	1	0.4	—	—
Undetermined	2	0.6	—	—
TOTAL	312	100.0	210	100.0

Figure 30

SUMMARY

ACCIDENTS, FATAL ACCIDENTS
AND RATES

High-Wing vs. Low-Wing*

1968 – 1969

(Average)

	HIGH-WING		LOW-WING	
	Total Accidents	Fatal Accidents	Total Accidents	Fatal Accidents
Fire after impact	115	78	169	103
No fire after impact	2,583	259	1,739	175
TOTAL	2,698	337	1,908	278
Fatal accidents as a percent of total accidents		12.49		14.57
TOTAL ACTIVE AIRCRAFT		68,700		46,200
Aircraft involved in accidents as a percent of total aircraft	3.92	0.49	4.12	0.60
TOTAL HOURS FLOWN		13,531,000		9,320,000
RATE PER 100,000 HOURS	19.93	2.49	20.47	2.98

*No official accident data relative to high-wing and low-wing airplanes is available. The statistics shown in this table are computed on the basis of ratio between single- and multi-engine aircraft vs. high-wing and low-wing aircraft as shown on page 53 and in Figures 26 and 27.

59

Statistical Findings

1. General aviation flying was much safer at the end of the sixties than at the beginning of the decade. However, during the period 1966 through 1969, the safety records in general aviation flying did not show a significant improvement. Fatal accident rate remained at about 0.175 per million aircraft miles; fatality rate remained at 17-18 deaths per one hundred million passenger miles; aircraft loss rate remained in the neighborhood of 0.30 aircraft per million miles or one aircraft loss per 21,000 to 23,000 aircraft hours flown.

2. According to NTSB preliminary statistics for 1970, general aviation fatalities in 1970 were 15% lower than the previous year and fatal accident rate was 12% lower than the average of the previous five years. However, as to the number of total accidents and fatalities, the figure for 1970 is still slightly higher than the previous five-year average.

3. Fatalities and serious injuries as a percent of total pilots and passengers aboard the aircraft involved in accidents have shown an upward trend since 1962.

4. Over the years 1968 and 1969, there was no significant change of accident distribution in phase-of-operation. Approach and landing accidents accounted for 50% of total accidents while in-flight accidents and takeoff accidents accounted for 25% and 18% respectively.

5. In all types of aircraft, including single-engine, multi-engine, high-wing and low-wing aircraft, the pilot was cited most often as the cause of an accident while weather and terrain were cited more often as a related factor.

6. Fire involvement in accidents over the years 1962-1969 showed an increasing trend. Of the accidents involving fire, over 61% were fatal and over 93% of the aircraft involved were destroyed. Of the no-fire accidents 11% were fatal and 18% of the aircraft involved were destroyed.

7. Fire involvement also affected the survivability of the persons aboard aircraft. Of the total aboard aircraft involving fire, 62% were fatally injured while only 10.6% of the total aboard aircraft involved in no-fire accidents were fatally injured. In the latter case the aircraft involved were either destroyed or substantially damaged.

8. If fire did occur after impact and the aircraft involved was destroyed, the probability of survival of the persons aboard the aircraft was three out of 10. If fire did not occur after impact but the aircraft destroyed, the probability of survival was increased to five out of 10.

9. In terms of exposure, the accident rate for single-engine aircraft is much higher than that of multi-engine-aircraft. However, the fatal accident rate for single-engine aircraft is slightly lower. In terms of fire involvement, aircraft damage, injury index, there is no substantial difference in safety performance between single-engine aircraft and multi-engine aircraft.

10. Although proportionately more low-wing aircraft than high-wing aircraft were involved in accidents wherein fire after impact occurred, there is no significant difference in safety between high-wing and low-wing aircraft.

8. Crashworthiness

Crashworthiness is the capability of the aircraft to provide a greater degree of human survivability under accident and impact conditions. It has been the subject of expanded attention over the last few years, both for aircraft and automobiles.

Major steps in improving aircraft crashworthiness, following the classic work[16] on injury causes by De Haven in the early 1940s, include:

a. The development of the CAA-Texas A&M College agricultural airplane by Fred Weick in 1950. This airplane incorporated a number of original crashworthiness features which have since become almost standard in production agricultural airplanes (page 63).

b. The airplane crash/fire tests conducted by the NASA Lewis laboratory.[17]

c. The FAA full-scale crash tests of a DC-7 and L-1049 at the FSF AvSER facility at Phoenix in 1964.[18]

d. The in-depth study of particular general aviation airplane accidents by Swearingen.[19]

e. U.S. Army support of work to develop and correlate crash survival design information.[20]

As discussed in the introduction to this report, public attention recently has been drawn to the subject of crashworthiness by the exchange of views between the Chairman of the National Transportation Safety Board, the Administrator of the Federal Aviation Administration, and other activity.

In the crashworthiness phase of this study of safety in general aviation, FSF drew on the experience and judgement of members of the Society of

---

[16] De Haven, Hugh — Causes of Injuries in Light Plane Accidents. Aero Digest Aviation Engineering, March 1, 1944.

[17] Pinkel, I.I., Preston, G.M., and Pesman, G.J. — Mechanism of Start and Development of Aircraft Crash Fires. NACA Research Memorandum E52F06, August 1952.

[18] Reed, W.H., Robertson, S.H., Weinberg, L.W.T. and Tyndall, L.H. — Crash Tests of a Douglas DC-7, FAA Report ADS-37, April 1965 (L1649 ADS-38, October 1965).

[19] Swearingen, J.J., General Aviation Structures Directly Responsible for Trauma in Crash Decelerations. FAA special Report FAA-AM 71-3, January 1971.

[20] Turnbow, J.W., Carroll, D.F., Haley, J.L., Jr., Robertson, S.H., Crash Survival Design Guide. USAAVLABS Technical Report 70-22. Revised August 1969.

A MAJOR ADVANCE IN SAFETY
The CAA-Texas A&M Agricultural Airplane of 1950

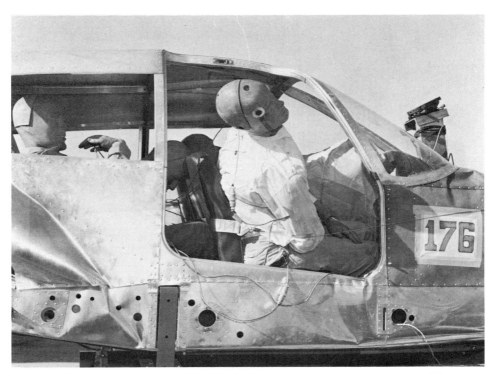

AIR BAG RESTRAINT SYSTEM TEST

Air Safety Investigators (SASI). The following questions were posed in a letter sent to all members.[21]

In potentially survivable general aviation accidents wherein there were fatalities or injuries:

1. List in order of priority for the cockpit/cabin environment and for fire following impact, the items which, in your experience, have produced the most fatalities or injuries.

2. List in order of priority improvements which could be made to reduce such fatalities and/or injuries.

3. List location, date and type of aircraft for accidents which you believe would yield useful information through detailed study.

The response was prompt and excellent, and the replies to the first two questions are tabulated below in order of priority.

Question 1: The items which have produced the most fatalities or injuries.

Order of Priority	Answers
1	Lack or improper use of occupant restraint
2	Fire after impact
3	Seat collapse
4	Airframe structure
5	Inadequate instrument panel/control panel
6	Inadequate emergency exit system
7	Dazed conditions/inability to evacuate
8	Loose objects/inadequate baggage restraint

[21]Letter dated October 12,1970, from the president of SASI to all members.

Question 2: Improvements which could be made to reduce fatalities or injuries.

Order of Priority	Answers
1	Occupant restraint
2	Seat design
3	Crash fire prevention
4	Airframe structure crashworthiness
5	Cockpit delethalization
6	Emergency exit system
7	Baggage restraint

Improvements in crashworthiness are mainly dependent upon improvement in three basic areas:

1. **Deceleration:** Holding peak deceleration of the occupant portion of the aircraft to the minimum value for the available distance in which stoppage occurs.

2. **Packaging:** Protecting and restraining the human occupant to remain within survivable limits of load, deceleration versus time, and local pressure.

3. **Postcrash Fire:** Preventing combustion of flammable fluids by containment, reduction in their ambient flammability and separation of such fluids from ignition sources. Ease of evacuation also is an element but its importance in general aviation aircraft is less than in transport airplanes.

These areas are discussed in some detail in the following sections.

Deceleration

The magnitude of impact of a moving object can be reduced by absorbing it through a distance, whether it be a baseball into a catcher's mitt, a car into a hedge instead of against a wall, or other phenomena. The physical relationships are shown in *Figure 31*. For example, from a speed of 40 mph

(64 kmh) which is equivalent to the velocity attained in a free fall of 53 feet, a stop in one foot (30 cm) results in a probably lethal deceleration force of 53.7 g, stopping in two feet (61 cm) is 26.9 g and if the deceleration can be stretched out to eight feet (2.4|m), a relatively modest deceleration of 6.72 g results.

The values shown in *Figure 31* and those cited above assume constant deceleration which is extremely difficult to realize in actual cases. For a given velocity and stopping distance, a lower deceleration throughout part of the stopping distance will result in a higher than average force in other portions of the stopping distance. Because of the random nature of impact, direction and force in actual accidents, and the necessity of meeting the structural loading conditions for flight and ground operation in the most efficient manner, it is difficult to arrange the structural elements of the aircraft to approach uniform deceleration under impact conditions.

In the rather specialized case of the design of an agricultural airplane *(page 62)*, it was possible to provide a substantial deceleration distance. The pilot was placed well aft and high in a narrow fuselage for good visibility, and the disposable load was positioned in front of him at the center of gravity of the airplane. In current general aviation airplanes it is impractical to use this arrangement. Here, the pilot is positioned as far forward as possible to provide him with the best field of vision and to allow the passengers to be positioned well forward because of balance considerations.

Some alleviation of the effect of impact velocity can be obtained by deflecting the aircraft into a different path. For example, an aircraft descending at a 30° angle to the surface at a speed of 80 mph (129 kmh) would have a vertical speed component of 40 mph (65 kmh). If this component could be absorbed through crumpling of the lower fuselage by a little over two feet (61 cm), the deceleration of the occupants might be held

Figure 31

EFFECT OF
STOPPING DISTANCE
ON
IMPACT "G" FORCE

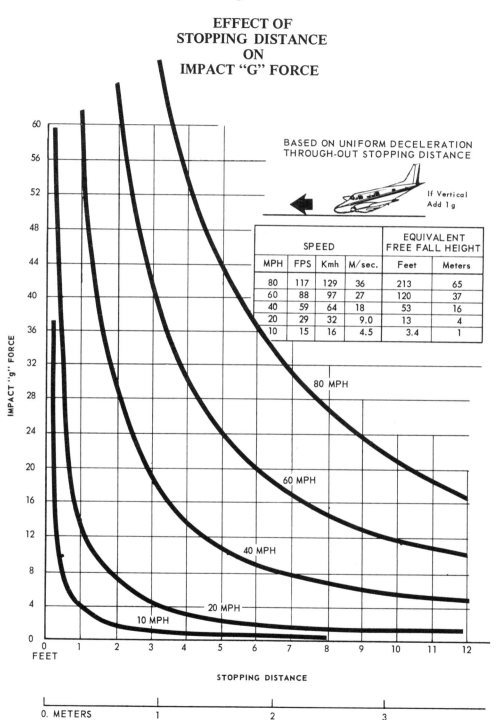

BASED ON UNIFORM DECELERATION
THROUGH-OUT STOPPING DISTANCE

If Vertical
Add 1 g

	SPEED			EQUIVALENT FREE FALL HEIGHT	
MPH	FPS	Kmh	M/sec.	Feet	Meters
80	117	129	36	213	65
60	88	97	27	120	37
40	59	64	18	53	16
20	29	32	9.0	13	4
10	15	16	4.5	3.4	1

IMPACT "g" FORCE

80 MPH

60 MPH

40 MPH

20 MPH

10 MPH

STOPPING DISTANCE

FEET

0. METERS

to less than 25 g, thus offering greater chance of survivability. Additionally, the horizontal component of speed of 69 mph (111 kmh) could be absorbed over a distance by sliding friction which would further add to chances of survivability. Shaping and reinforcement of the lower forward portions of the fuselage may facilitate the change in direction by preventing abrupt "digging in" to the surface.

Packaging

Of first importance in packaging is proper support and restraint of the aircraft occupant within the surrounding structure. Seat belts, shoulder harness, nets and other means have been used or proposed. Even with these torso restraint systems, flailing of the head, arms and legs may occur during deceleration. Hence the importance of eliminating or adequately padding structural members or heavy masses within the flailing area. The principles which apply to head protection[20] also apply here. Considerable research and testing have been done on restraint systems and the determinations of tolerable decelerations on the body. Standard terminology has been established for the direction of applied force on the occupant as shown in *Figure 32*. The g values listed indicate maximum tolerable deceleration, i.e., no injury, for military personnel using maximum body support.

Figure 32

DIRECTION OF DECELERATIVE FORCE
From Reference 20

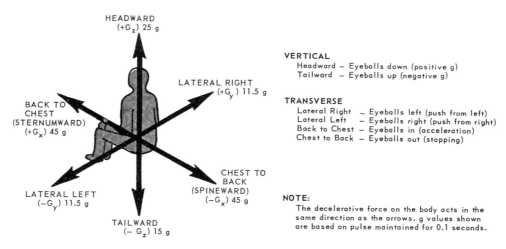

VERTICAL
  Headward – Eyeballs down (positive g)
  Tailward – Eyeballs up (negative g)

TRANSVERSE
  Lateral Right – Eyeballs left (push from left)
  Lateral Left – Eyeballs right (push from right)
  Back to Chest – Eyeballs in (acceleration)
  Chest to Back – Eyeballs out (stopping)

NOTE:
  The decelerative force on the body acts in the same direction as the arrows. g values shown are based on pulse maintained for 0.1 seconds.

HEADWARD
($+G_z$) 25 g

LATERAL RIGHT
($+G_y$) 11.5 g

BACK TO CHEST
(STERNUMWARD)
($+G_x$) 45 g

LATERAL LEFT
($-G_y$) 11.5 g

CHEST TO BACK
(SPINEWARD)
($-G_x$) 45 g

TAILWARD
($-G_z$) 15 g

Duration of force application. The duration of application of force is important. The human body can safely withstand very high g forces if the duration is short. While the specific relationships will vary with the direction of the force as well as with the individual and the circumstances, the approximate range of variation of tolerable acceleration with the duration of the pulse for "headward" acceleration is as shown in *Figure 33.*

The rate of onset of the applied force has a definite, though not yet well understood effect on human tolerance.

Figure 33

DURATION AND MAGNITUDE OF HEADWARD ACCELERATION ENDURED BY VARIOUS SUBJECTS – From Reference 20

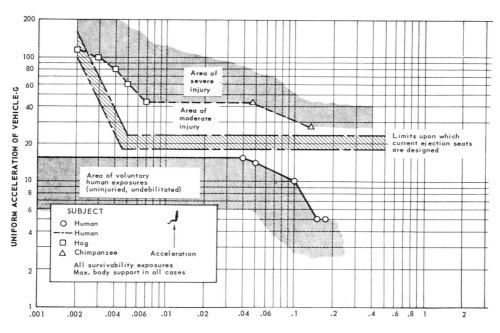

DURATION OF UNIFORM ACCELERATION

Protection of the head is vital under impact conditions. Pioneering work by Swearingen[22] has provided considerable data on survivable deceleration values and unit pressures. *Figure 34* indicates this. For example, load well distributed over the forehead would allow the head to be decelerated at 200 g. If we assume the area shown to be 3 square inches (19.2 cm^2) and the head weight as 10.5 pounds (4.76 kg), the forehead will withstand unit pressures of around 700 psi (49 kg/cm^2).

Figure 34

TOLERANCE OF HUMAN FACE TO IMPACT

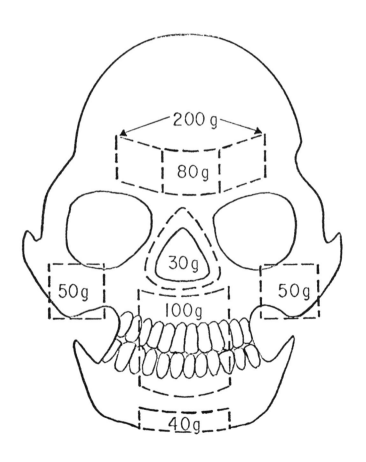

[22]Swearingen, J.J. — Tolerances of the Human Face to Crash Impact. FAA Report AM-65-20, July 1965.

While a considerable effort has been devoted to studies of crash-worthiness, there is very little specific information in the reports of fatal accidents in general aviation as to the cause of death, whether it be heart failure, impact trauma, burns, carbon monoxide, or other. Siegel[23] has done some work in this area. More complete and concise reporting would aid in developing design changes and improved standards.

Crash Fire

As shown in *Figure 18* (page 40), if an accident involves fire there are almost two chances out of three of a fatality. Without fire, the chance of fatality drops to nearly one out of 10. Obviously, part of the increased hazard is due to the severe impact which caused the fire, but elimination of fire would substantially improve safety. Also the SASI replies, page 64, indicate fire after impact as the second largest cause of fatalities and injuries.

Engine Type and Fuel Flammability. For the most part general aviation aircraft are powered by piston engines, with only a relatively few using turbines. The turbine engine can use low-volatility fuel such as kerosene, but the piston engine requires gasoline which is flammable over a much wider range of ambient conditions. Until the cost-per-horsepower of turbines is greatly reduced the piston engine will continue to power the great majority of general aviation aircraft.

Emergency Evacuation. Somewhat lower on the scale of hazards in case of fire is delay in emergency evacuation. Even though kerosene is generally used in transport aircraft, speed of evacuation is of vital importance because the many occupants must leave through a small number of exits often high above the ground. In transport aircraft even the interior trim materials can be a hazard by generating smoke and toxic fumes in burning.

The condition is somewhat less severe in general aviation aircraft but the flashfire nature of gasoline on ignition makes rapid evacuation very important. The flame-resistance and toxicity of interior materials is of less importance, except with respect to in-flight fire, e.g., resulting from cigarettes. It is of interest on this latter point that the original 1926 Air Commerce Regulations (page 6) specified that there be on board and in operating condition "fire-extinguishing equipment, of a design approved by the Secretary of Commerce." None is required now. A phase of the evacuation problem is that of occupants trapped in wreckage, due either to jamming of exits or collapse of structure.

---

[23]P.V. Siegel, S.R. Mohler, A. Cierebiej, The Safety Significance of Aircraft Post Mortem Findings. Report AM 69-18, FAA, Washington, October 1969

Fuel Containment. Considerable work has been done by the FAA, the military services and industry on the crash fire problem. Improvements in containment and in means or changes to reduce the possibility of fuel ignition should substantially improve the safety record. U.S. Army experience indicates this:[24]

"The U.S. Army Board for Aviation Accident Research recently conducted an analysis of 104 mishaps involving crashworthy fuel system-equipped helicopters which occurred during the period 23 June 1970 to 28 February 1971. These included 13 major accidents, 30 incidents, 16 forced landings, and 45 precautionary landings. There were two nonthermal fatal injuries and 15 nonthermal serious and minor injuries involved in the 13 major accidents. It is significant that there were no thermal injuries or fatalities resulting from any of these mishaps. All the data collected thus far discloses that when crashworthy fuel system-equipped helicopters are involved in mishaps, the chances of fire are greatly reduced. If fire does occur, there is enough time for the occupants to evacuate and avoid thermal injuries."

The crashworthy fuel system-equipped helicopters differed from other Army helicopters principally in that they had:

1. Semi-rigid fuel tanks fabricated with laminated synthetic material having highly puncture-resistant characteristics, and

2. Fuel lines with surplus length and self-sealing break-away fittings.

In addition to the FAA standards governing powerplant and flammable fluid installations, a considerable amount of information of use to designers is contained in the U.S. Army report Crash Survival Design Guide referred to earlier in ref. 20 on page 62.

Automobile vs. Aircraft Crashworthiness

There are a number of points of similarity between the crashworthiness problem in automobiles and general aviation airplanes.

1. The human body can withstand very large deceleration forces if properly restrained.

2. Occupant restraint systems have much in common.

---

[24]USABAAR Weekly Summary, 19-26 March 1971.

3. Elimination of sharp projections within the range of the rider greatly enhances his safety under impact conditions.

4. The capsule of structure surrounding the occupant may be designed to fail progressively and through absorption of energy in deformation and break-up, reduce the decelerating force acting on the occupant.

However, there also are a number of differences between the automobile and the airplane with respect to this problem. In the United States the automobile kills 55,000 persons per year and injures nearly 1,500,000*. While approximately 18% of the auto casualties are pedestrians, i.e., 9,800 of the 54,895 fatalities in 1969, the ratio of killed to injured is virtually unchanged. The operation of general aviation airplanes in the U.S. in 1969 resulted in 1,410 fatalities and only 697 seriously injured. Hence the automobile causes only one fatality for 27 cases of injury, while the airplane kills two persons for every one person injured. Or conversely, per fatality there are over 50 times the chance of injury in an automobile than in an airplane.

Figure 35 illustrates an important conclusion that may logically be drawn from the ratios just cited. The ordinate indicates severity of impact starting at "no injury" and rising to a "fatal" level and beyond. The abscissa is the number of people involved, or statistical population. While no strict mathematical relationship may be drawn from this figure, it is obvious that for the automobile, a slight increase in the allowable severity level, i.e., raising the "fatal" line, would greatly decrease the number of fatalities. The same action would have only a slight effect on the number of fatalities in the case of the airplane. There are many marginally fatal cases in auto accidents, few in airplanes.

In automobiles about 60% of impacts are within 30° left and right of straight ahead − 11 to 1 o'clock. Approximately 18% are aft impacts − 5 to 7 o'clock, with the remaining 22% rather evenly divided between left and right sides. The airplane occupant rarely is subjected to impact from the rear and he generally has good protection against lateral impact because of energy-absorption capabilities of the wings, the region where the automobile is least protected.

Approximately 400,000 of the 14 to 15 million automobile accidents involve fire (less than 3%). In 1969, 7% of the airplane accidents involved fire.

Structural weight reduction is of the highest importance in aircraft. With respect to automobiles, it places a low second to ease of production and low cost.

---

*NOTE: There is no federal definition of a disabling injury for use in motor vehicle statistics. The National Safety Council however, uses the American Standard Z16.1 i.e., "an injury which prevents a person from performing any of his usual activities for a full day beyond the day of the accident."

Figure 35

COMPARISON
OF
AUTOMOBILE & AIRCRAFT
FATALITY – INJURY RATES

APPROXIMATE VALUES
1969

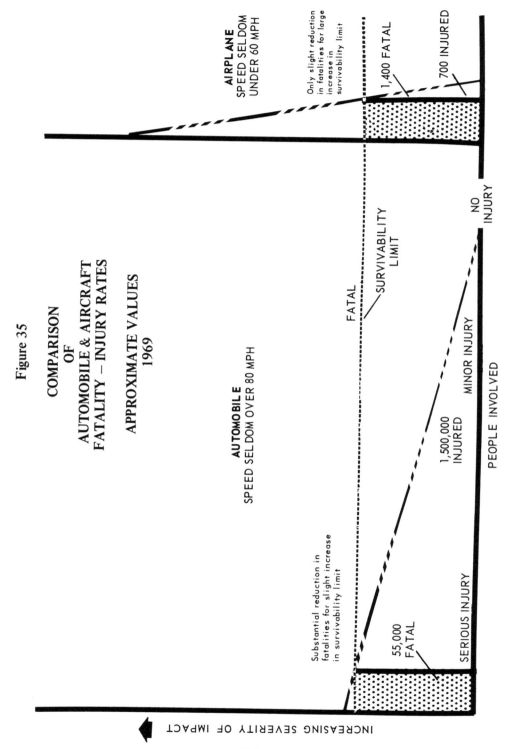

Because of the need for optimum visibility in aircraft, ease of reading instruments, and readily operating controls, there should be little compromise with any of the following:

1. Best possible field of vision which dictates a forward position for the pilot and narrow windshield posts with the resultant compromise of strength under impact conditions.

2. Optimum location of instruments which may place appreciable masses in front of the pilot.

3. Ease of handling controls, including radio knobs, etc., with gloved hands.

Suggestions have been made to eliminate the control column extending through the instrument panel since under severe impact conditions it has been known to impale the crew. However, a swinging column or arm may cause accidents. There is record of a microphone having jammed a floor-mounted column. Similarly, inadvertent operation of an air-bag safety system could push a primary control fore or aft, causing an immediate and total loss of control with fatal results.

In summary, while much can be learned from automobile experience, great care must be exercised in applying these lessons to aircraft lest improving crashworthiness reduce airworthiness, with an overall reduction in safety. The principal safety goal in aircraft must be to avoid accidents.

$\mathcal{9}._\circ$ ACCIDENTS AND THEIR PREVENTION

Many years ago, C. G. Grey, well-known British editor of The Aeroplane magazine, wrote "Aeroplanes should land slowly and not burn up." These basic points are still valid. While human failings are by far the greatest cause of accidents in general aviation, observance of the first of these principles — the ability to land slowly — would increase the pilot's time to make judgments and decisions in order to avoid accidents. Observance of the second principle — not burn up — would materially reduce the seriousness of the consequences of the accidents. There is, of course, much more to safety in aviation than this, and in this chapter various concepts will be explored.

Referring back to *Figure 16* (page 37) the leading causes and related factors in general aviation accidents are:

> Pilot
> Weather
> Mechanical
> Personnel — other than pilot
> Terrain
> Airport and Airway Facilities
> Miscellaneous

As has been noted earlier, when more than one cause or factor contributes to an accident the NTSB lists each factor. On an overall basis this amounts to an average of one and one-half causes per accident.

In the following discussion some of the cause/factors listed above are discussed under somewhat different headings to provide better continuity. The "mechanical" accidents are discussed in the aircraft section; "terrain" and "airport and airway facilities" are discussed under "airport" and "air traffic control" and "navigation". Typical accident cases are included to illustrate the problems.

Airmen

Over 80% of all accidents in general aviation are charged to pilot error as a cause or factor. Obviously, other cause/factors enter into many of these. However, the greatest potential for improvement in safety lies in the selection, training, continuing education and monitoring of the pilot population.

The U.S. FAA in its "Accident Prevention Program" is working with general aviation pilots to up-grade their knowledge and skill. The Aircraft Owners and Pilots Association conducts training and refresher courses in general aviation. The Flight Safety Foundation, which for 26 years served the airline, manufacturing and corporate community, has opened its membership and services to individuals for the purpose of providing safety information to the general aviation pilot.

One problem with any voluntary training program is that it is more successful with the conscientious pilot than the over-confident pilot who really needs it. However, a combination of the "carrot" of attractive voluntary refresher and rating courses of the type AOPA has pioneered, and the "stick" of stricter pilot certification and recertification procedures by FAA should yield substantial gains in safety.

In working on improving pilot skills and experience, there is one important aspect which constitutes a major problem. Half the U.S. population is licensed to operate motor vehicles, where most decisions are based on visual estimates of distance and speed. The aircraft pilot, however, operates in a fluid medium wherein decisions and control operation must be based not only on visual cues but upon kinesthetic sensing of speed, acceleration, angular motion, sound and other cues.

The overall problem has been well-stated by Lederer in reference 10 (page 9).

"Flying will always remain somewhat of an art, like boating, because of its variables — especially wind and weather. There will always be downwash in the lee of a mountain, for example. Flight training will continue to be more difficult than training for other types of private transportation if the aircraft is to serve as a personal cross-country vehicle. Nevertheless, the training, attention and skills now needed for safe flight are subject to reduction by further engineering technology.

"Airplane accidents in private flying often result from normal carelessness, complacency, impatience, spasmodic vigilance, or a lack of anticipation, but probably not to any greater degree than causes a person to burn toast, overeat or jay walk. Most accidents are the result of the ordinary frailties of mankind.

"The private pilot is just as forgetful, just as absent-minded, impetuous, awkward or nervous as anyone else. He does not always maintain top proficiency as a pilot. He often disregards elaborate instructions; and under conditions of stress he should not be expected to function as efficiently as a test pilot or an airline pilot. He does not always practice good airmanship, but he is the

77

man for whom the airplane should be designed, and for whom the infra-structure — should be tailored. This is the man who creates the challenge to the engineer: to reduce the necessary degree of skills, care and airmanship now required for safe flight by the private pilot.

"Similar problems in human factors have been accepted by engineers in other fields, notably the design of shop machinery, the design of thruways, household appliances. The airplane presents more of a challenge. Accidents are prevented by improving conditions rather than relying so much on operator attitudes, training, and constant alertness."

Examining some specific accident cases, the accident which took the life of a retired heavyweight boxing champion illustrates how inexperience can have tragic consequences.

Case I: INEXPERIENCE[25]   Iowa, summer, 1969

The pilot of the four-place high-wing airplane had been given an adequate weather briefing at Chicago Midway airport before takeoff at 6:00 p.m. on his flight to Des Moines, Iowa, some 300 miles (480 km) to the west. With him were two passengers, one of them the retired boxing champion.

The pilot was told of a frontal system near Des Moines and enroute weather which occasionally would include ceilings below 1,000 feet and visibilities below two miles. The forecast also included scattered thunderstorms. The pilot, holder of a private pilot license, was qualified only for VFR flight with its basic weather minimums of 1,000-foot ceiling and three miles visibility. He was not instrument qualified for IFR. His total flying time was 231 hours, 107 of which had been in the type of aircraft being flown on this trip, and 35 at night.

Almost three hours after takeoff the pilot requested Des Moines Radar Approach Control assistance in locating the Des Moines airport under a cloud layer. Soon thereafter he reported he was over an airport east of Des Moines and would land there to refuel. At the radar controller's request, the pilot verified his position over the latter airport, flying VFR, and reported that he had the airport in sight. This was the pilot's last known transmission.

A witness some two miles south of the airport saw the aircraft at an altitude he estimated not to be over 100 feet (30 m). He said it pulled up and disappeared into low clouds, reappeared about 10 or 15 seconds

---

[25]NTSB Release No. SB 69-82, dated October 10, 1969.

78

later, descended, then made a climbing left turn. After reaching a vertical bank, the aircraft seemed to fall off toward the ground, he said. The aircraft disappeared from the witness's view near a hill where the wreckage later was found. There were no survivors and no post-crash fire.

The Safety Board's examination of the wreckage revealed no pre-impact mechanical failure or malfunction of the aircraft. There was fuel in both main tanks, tank caps were secured, the fuel selector was positioned to draw fuel from both tanks. No physiological conditions related to accident cause were found.

The NTSB determined that the pilot had attempted operation exceeding his experience/ability level, continued Visual Flight Rules (VFR) flight into adverse weather conditions, and experienced spatial disorientation in the last moments of the flight. Low ceiling and a dark night were cited as contributing factors.

One element difficult to evaluate is that of the judgment and discipline of the pilot. The following case is taken from an accident report by the Australian Department of Civil Aviation.[26]

Case II: OPERATIONAL INEXPERIENCE   New Guinea, May 1970

At 8:30 a.m., an eight-place twin-engine low-wing airplane, carrying nine persons (one a child) in a charter operation, started takeoff from a small, near sea-level airport. The takeoff roll was aborted due to failure of the right engine. On the third attempt, the engine was started and the airplane took off. It failed to reach its destination and after 10 days of extensive search the burned-out wreckage was discovered close to the point of departure but in dense jungle some 2,200 feet (670 m) above sea level and 250 feet (76 m) below the lowest point of a saddle or gap in a ridge to be traversed. From tree damage, etc., in the jungle, it was determined that the aircraft descended along a 16-degree path and in a 90-degree banked left turn. All on board were fatally injured.

Calculations indicate the airplane was overloaded some 5% and the c.g. was about 0.3% aft of the rear limit. The pilot had 1,272 hours total flying time, 19 hours on the particular type aircraft involved in the accident, which was also his first endorsement on a multi-engine aircraft. He did not hold an instrument rating. There is uncertainty as to whether the ridge was obscured by clouds at the time of the accident.

---

[26]Accident Investigation Report 70-1, October 1970.

The Australian investigating authorities concluded that "the flight path which the pilot attempted to follow would have provided only a marginal terrain clearance even if it had been flown under optimum conditions of aircraft and pilot performance and without any adverse environmental effects." They found the probable cause of this accident was that "the pilot, who was inexperienced in the operational circumstances which pertained, did not make a timely decision to turn away from rising terrain when it should have been apparent that the aircraft could not clear it."

In this case the effects of poor judgment and inexperience on the part of the pilot were compounded by possible power deterioration or loss and weather.

One of the most interesting studies[27] in pilot training in accident prevention was made by Dr. John D. Dougherty, Assistant Professor of Environmental Health and Safety, Harvard School of Public Health. His study concluded that the annual overall general aviation accident rates vary through limits far exceeding those expected from chance. This variation is closely associated with the proportion of pilots not known to have been in training. *The fatal accidents* also varied widely and *are closely related to the proportion of pilots not known to be recently or currently engaged in training.* These associations support the hypothesis that continued periodic flight training of all pilots would result in a large reduction of both the overall and fatal accident rates.

Pilots should be encouraged to take periodic refresher checks from a certificated flight instructor who can catch their bad habits and nip them before they become an accident. Airline and military pilots must take check rides every six months despite the fact that they may have 25,000 hours and cross the Atlantic or Pacific every week. There must be a reason.

A wise, experienced head of safety education of a military service was asked what single piece of advice he would pass on to pilots who wanted to do a better job. His reply was, "Be circumspect." This advice becomes clear from the dictionary definition, which is:

"Attention to, or marked by attention to, all the circumstances of a case, or the probable consequences of an action; watchful on every side; cautious; prudent; wary."

There is no better advice for anyone — student or senior airline captain.

---

[27]Dr. John D. Dougherty. Pilot Training and Accident Prevention. 23rd Annual International Air Safety Seminar, FSF, Washington D.C., October 1970.

Improved training, rechecks and thorough dissemination of safety information on a trial basis by the FAA in the Southwest U.S. produced a 30% reduction in fatal accidents.[28]

An important element of periodic check-ups is the competence of the flight instructor. Here, there also is need to improve the standards and stature of the instructor. Too often the position of general aviation flight instructor is but a way station for the young pilot interested in attaining an airline pilot's position, and the hourly remuneration is less than that of a golf professional. It is unfortunate that some of the money now spent on litigation, as shown on page 10, could not be devoted to a constructive program of improving training and instruction.

LeVier,[29] has pointed out:

> "Some of the best-qualified instructors are now airplane captains, test pilots, crop dusters, executive pilots or pipe-line and power-line patrol flyers. If they had their choice, many of them would choose flight instruction because it is one of the most rewarding and personally satisfying jobs in aviation. But they have families, homes and all the responsibilities the average man has and flight instruction simply doesn't pay the freight. Steps should be taken to establish legal minimum hourly rates which are high enough to provide an income commensurate with the skills and training required for flight instruction."

Alcohol. A cause/factor of significance in accidents is impairment of efficiency or judgment, or incapacitation of the pilot. An NTSB study[30] indicates that during the three-year period 1967 through 1969, alcohol was a cause factor in 6 to 7 percent of U.S. general aviation accidents. Alcohol is listed as a cause/factor in only 1 percent of all, i.e., non-fatal as well as fatal accidents, hence piloting while under the influence of alcohol greatly increases the possibility of a serious accident.

It is probable that some of the habits and attitudes of vehicle drivers with respect to drinking have been carried over into general aviation. While the drinking pilot is probably less of a hazard to third parties than the drinking driver, he is certainly a much greater risk to himself and any passengers unfortunate enough to accompany him. A recent FAA aeromedical study[31] indicates the seriousness of the degradation of performance in pilot-type tasks.

---

[28] W.E. Berkebile, FAA Accident Prevention Program Review, FSF International Air Safety Seminar, October 1970, Washington, D.C.

[29] A.W. "Tony" LeVier. Approach to Safety Problems. FSF 16th Annual Corporate Aircraft Safety Seminar, Arlington, Va. April 1971.

[30] NTSB Briefs of Accidents, Issue No. 1, 1970.

[31] Alcohol and Disorientation-Related Responses, FAA-AM-71-20, April 1971.

Little information is available as to the frequency of physical impairment in flight due to heart attack, strokes, gastrointestinal trouble or other physical ailment. It is probably of low order.

Weather

As previously pointed out *(page 35)*, from the standpoint of pilot-involvement in fatal accidents, the most common cause is failure to obtain/maintain flying speed. Following this are:

> Continued VFR into adverse weather
> Inadequate pre-flight preparation and planning
> Improper IFR operation
> Spatial disorientation
> Attempted operation beyond experience/ability

It is obvious that most of these cause factors involve weather. In serious accidents the weather encountered, in order of frequency, were 1) low ceiling, 2) fog, and 3) rain. In less serious accidents, wherein the aircraft were not destroyed, the weather was 1) unfavorable wind conditions, 2) conditions conducive to carburetor/induction system icing, and 3) low ceiling.

An excellent study of weather for the pilot as he must deal with it has been written by Buck[32].

In a 1968 study[33], the NTSB found that 1) the pilot was a cause or factor in 97.86 percent of the 1966 weather-involved fatal accidents, 2) the pilot had not obtained a weather briefing in 22.99 percent of these fatal accidents, and 3) 84.05 percent of the forecasts that were known to have been available proved to be substantially correct.

Examples of serious accidents involving weather include:

Case I: INADEQUATE PREPARATION   Indiana, 1968

At 7:40 p.m. on a winter night, a lightplane pilot who had logged 666 total hours but was not rated for instrument flight, took off with one passenger from an Indiana airport bound for an Ohio airport, 35 miles (56 km) to the southeast. About 30 minutes prior to his takeoff the

---

[32] Robert M. Buck, Weather Flying, MacMillan 1970.
[33] NTSB Release No. SB 69-6, dated January 24, 1969.

airport weather had been observed as "visibility less than one mile (1.6 km), ground fog," and an apparent "very low" ceiling. An aviation weather forecast for the general time and area of the takeoff had predicted ceilings below 1,000 feet (305 m) and visibility below two miles (3.2 km).

About five minutes after takeoff, the pilot radioed an air traffic control radar facility at Dayton, Ohio, for help in coping with "a tremendous fog." Three minutes later the pilot reported his artificial horizon inoperative. Since his aircraft also had an electrically operated turn-and-bank indicator, the pilot was advised to turn from his 180-degree heading to 360 degrees. He said he would make the turn. When told that cloud tops in his area were about 1,000 to 2,000 feet (305 to 610 m) above him, the pilot reported he would start a climb.

One minute later he radioed: "Ah, yeah, I just almost had it," and then, "I think I'm going to crash." The airplane struck the ground 16 miles south of the airport of origin, killing both the pilot and his passenger. There was no impact fire. Examination of the wreckage by NTSB investigators showed no evidence of pre-impact mechanical failure or malfunction, and the Board said the weather conditions the plane had entered were "highly conducive" to icing within the system which provides necessary air flow for certain flight instruments.

The investigation also disclosed no evidence that the pilot had obtained a weather briefing for his flight.

The NTSB determined that the probable cause was inadequate preparation, operation beyond experience level and spatial disorientation.

Case II: TOO MUCH WEATHER   Arkansas, 1971

This accident involved low visibility, low ceiling, icing and strong winds.

About 7:45 a.m. the pilot, a dental surgeon with around 800 total hours, some 400 hours in the particular airplane and the holder of a private pilot's license with an instrument-rating, took off from his home airport in a six-place, single-engine, low-wing airplane. He had five passengers with him. He filed an instrument flight plan to an airport 70 miles (112 km) to the east, and was briefed on the weather. During flight he requested a change from his assigned altitude of 5,000 feet to 7,000 feet because of icing. There was no further word until 8:42 a.m. when he contacted the FAA Flight Service Station (FSS) at his destination, reporting he was on the downwind leg for runway 36. There was no tower at the airport.

The surface weather observations, recorded at the FSS at 7:55 a.m., were:

Estimated 400-foot (122 m) overcast, visibility one mile (1.6 km) with very light rain and fog, temperature 36°F and dewpoint 35°F. The wind was 310°, altimeter setting of 29.73.

At 8:48 a.m. the wind was given as 310°, with a velocity of 20 knots, gusting to 28 knots.

A witness observed the aircraft on the downwind leg, flying in and out of scud-type clouds. After passing the southern boundary of the airport, the aircraft was observed making a left turn toward the east, a turn the pilot kept tightening because the wind pushed the airplane past the point to turn on final approach for runway 36. The aircraft then appeared to stall. It disappeared from view in a 45° nose-down, left-wing-down attitude. Clear ice was found on the aircraft and broken sheets of ice lay under the wreckage. The ice from the wing leading edge was about ½ to ¾ inch (12 to 19 mm) thick. There were no survivors and no fire.

Another witness about one mile south of the accident site observed the aircraft and added that it was raining, snowing and sleeting at the time.

It is probable that the airframe ice and tightened turn contributed to an accelerated stall.

The solution to the weather problem is three-fold:

1. Develop more pilot respect for adverse weather as a major threat to safety. Some progress is being made here.

2. Develop aircraft and instrumentation which allow safe flight in flyable weather by most if not all certificated pilots. This is discussed in the section on aircraft (page 96).

3. Provide accurate, up-to-the-minute and easily visualized information for the pilot, both before and during flight. On the short-term basis, up-grading of the FAA Flight Service Stations will help[34]. On a long-term basis, the weather facilities, the ground stations and the pilots aloft must be utilized in a coordinated and automated manner to attain the objective.

A satisfactory solution to these three phases, while simple in concept, represents a formidable task.

---

[34] Richard L. Collins, How to Put More Service in Flight Service Stations — Flying magazine, April 1971.

84

Navigation and Air Traffic Control

The original navigation system of lighted airways in the U.S. gave way in the late 1920's and early 1930's to a low-frequency 200-400 kilocycle band (originally designated as kc, now as kHz) four-course navigation system, and a low-frequency (3 - 6 mHz) communication system. Electronic glide slope guidance for landing in low-visibility conditions was first brought into civil use in 1946. The very high frequency (VHF) omni-range and communication system (108-127 mHz) was put into use by the then CAA in 1946.

A number of Presidentially-ordered studies of civil aviation have been made, particularly with respect to the air traffic and navigation system. Technical organizations have studied the problems and recommended action.

At this time in the U.S., the FAA employs 25,000 people in air traffic control work and 15,000 as technicians to install and maintain the system. The system and the airspace is used by some 3,000 air carrier aircraft, 15,000 military and 130,000 general aviation aircraft. It is difficult to consider continuing to add government personnel as the rate of one for each four aircraft added to the system. In 1970, however, 3,000 new controllers were hired and 8,000 new aircraft were produced.

The recently completed Department of Transportation-NASA study *(footnote 12, page 15)* contains the following recommendation:

"Since general aviation, the principal user of the airspace, will continue to grow at a rapid pace, safety and better control in crowded airspace is essential to facilitate flow and reduce congestion. It is recommended, therefore, that a four-step program be initiated leading to a fully cooperative air traffic control system. The Federal Government should (1) perform the necessary R&D to develop the standards required of avionics manufacturers by the end of 1972, (2) by the end of 1973, all newly manufactured aircraft should be equipped with a cooperative device manufactured to Government standards, (3) by 1980, all aircraft flying in the areas of the 30 primary hubs should be required to have such a device, and (4) by 1985 all users in the system should meet this specification. Certain special categories of general aviation aircraft, such as crop dusters, could be exempted from this requirement at the discretion of the FAA Adminstrator. Many general aviation users have voluntarily purchased transponders (about 40,000), and the rate of acceptance is increasing. However, this proposed regulation is believed essential to bring the entire system up to a capability which will permit greater automation and eventual retirement of the costly primary radar system."

Although pilotage (i.e., navigation by visual reference to cultural and terrain features on the surface of the earth) is a basic method of navigation under good weather conditions, under most conditions safety is enhanced by using electronic methods of navigation. Two-way communications are no longer a luxury but are a necessity in many locations with control towers. Pictorial displays will assist in navigation and automation may assist in communication.

Since the limiting factors in the purchase and use of airborne electronics are price, weight, size and power requirements, the continuing need in general aviation is for lightweight, low-cost and reliable navigation and communication equipment which is simple to understand and to operate. It is unfortunate that a recent federal statute now requires the installation of rescue beacons on all general aviation aircraft. Conceivably, this device could save half a dozen lives in one year. However, the same cost, weight and power (probably of the order of $100, one pound and 10 watts respectively) devoted to an anti-collision device might provide a key element in a national cooperative system for collision avoidance, thus eliminating a hazard to all air travelers.

Obviously, safety of operations in the vicinity of airports would be enhanced by uniformity of traffic flow. In the U.S., the FAA is working to formalize and amplify present procedures to create standard traffic rules for all aircraft approaching to land at airports without control towers. The proposal[35] would establish a rectangular pattern with all aircraft at 1,000 feet (305 m) above the airport elevation, until further descent is required for landing. Pattern entry procedure and limiting speeds are also included.

Guidance to the runway is discussed under the section on Airports starting on page 91.

As the number of general aviation aircraft increases and utility is improved to permit and facilitate operation under lower weather minima, the possibility of mid-air collision will increase. To the already difficult problem of developing proximity warning indicators (PWI) and collision avoidance system (CAS), and putting them into use in air carrier operation, must be added the formidable tasks of reducing weight, complexity and cost to encourage installation in general aviation aircraft.

It appears that pilot alertness and the maximum usable degree of separation of traffic, i.e., general aviation from the remaining traffic particularly in terminal areas, will be the best solution to the problem of collision for sometime to come.

The following three accident cases indicate some of the limitations of the general aviation pilot, the controller and the equipment, both airborne and ground, and of the airline pilot, that may be encountered in the operation of the ATC/NAV system.

---

[35]FAA Notice 71-20.

Case I: NAVIGATIONAL ERROR[36]   France, March 1968

At 7:23 p.m. a four-place twin-engine, low-wing airplane carrying four persons took off from an airport south of London for Clermont-Ferrand, France some 400 miles (645 km) to the south-southeast. The 25-year-old pilot had accumulated 544 hours, including 40 hours instrument flight and 26 hours night operation. He had logged 147 hours in this particular type aircraft and held an assistant instructor's rating but not an instrument rating. He had flown nearly three hours during that afternoon and would fly another 3.3 hours on this final flight.

The meteorological information given the pilot by telephone shortly before takeoff was:

A weak ridge over the south of England and France was moving eastward, giving rise to a westerly air stream over the route.

The cloud system over the route would consist of cumulus and strato-cumulus, base between 3,000 and 4,000 feet and tops between 5,000 and 7,000 feet.

Some development in the situation during the evening was forecast and the base of the lowest cloud would be broken, the medium cloud thickening between 8,000 and 14,000 feet.

Wind at 10,000 feet — 280°/30 knots becoming 300°/35 knots; altitude of 0°C isotherm-3,000 feet, becoming 4,000 feet; icing, moderate in cloud.

During the flight, the weather near the intended destination was given as:

Wind, 200°/9 knots; visibility, 20 km; cloud, 1/8 at 800 m, 7/8 at 1,400 m; surface temperature, 8° C.

The conditions encountered were approximately those forecast.

The pilot's flight plan was prepared on the basis of a route via Dieppe on the French coast, Mantes and Rambouillet (west and southwest of Paris), and then generally southeast to Clermont-Ferrand. When contacted, Paris control instructed the pilot to fly a route somewhat to the west of that planned, with different check points, and "this caused the pilot a certain amount of difficulty." Icing conditions were encountered after passing the French coast and during the remainder of the flight

---

[36]Taken from the translation of the report by the French Inspectorate General of Civil Aviation. British Board of Trade Report. No. CAP 319, 1969.

several changes of altitude were requested and granted. The pilot "did not give the impression of any great experience in the use of IFR procedures . . . the communications equipment . . . seemed to be defective . . . "

At approximately 10:40 p.m. the aircraft, while descending for a landing, struck a mountainside 22 miles (35 km) southwest of the intended destination. All occupants were killed; there was no fire. The point of impact was at an elevation of 5,000 feet (1,510 meters) and the snow-covered ground had a slope of about 35 degrees.

The very thorough accident investigation showed that while sufficient navigational aids were available in the aircraft to permit carrying out an instrument approach, both VHF communication/navigation sets had "failed in their communications function" as a result of the excessively high temperature to which they were subjected, "the cooling circuit having been obstructed by ice."

The French authorities found the cause of the accident to be "a navigational error during descent in icing conditions before landing at Clermont-Ferrand. During this descent the pilot did not succeed in carrying out an approach procedure because he was without any means of communication and also because of his limited experience and probably his anxiety and fatigue."

Case II: MISIDENTIFICATION[37]   California, spring, 1969

A twin-engine low-wing aircraft, carrying five persons on a flight from Albuquerque, New Mexico to an airport in California, was being vectored under positive radar control for an instrument approach to the destination airport by the FAA approach control facility at March Air Force Base. Weather in the destination area was partial obscuration, estimated ceiling 2,000 feet (610 m), visibility 1½ miles (24 km), haze and smoke.

Another aircraft, a two-place single-engine high-wing aircraft was over-flying the airport at a higher altitude at approximately the same time as the twin. Both aircraft would have been 4 to 5 miles (6.5 to 8 km) east of the nearby VOR at the same time, on a converging flight path but with adequate vertical separation. The targets of the two aircraft on converging courses presumably merged into one target on the radarscope as control was being transferred from one controller to another.

---

[37]NTSB Release No. SB70-65, dated August 26, 1970.

As the two aircraft targets again separated and continued along divergent courses, the second controller failed to identify the proper target. He finally realized that he was observing the wrong target and instructed the crew of the twin to turn to 20 degrees heading, and then to make a 360-degree turn, presumably to assist him in identifying the proper target on his radarscope.

The pilot, though unaware that radar contact was obviously lost, demonstrated his awareness and concern for the critical position in which he had been placed when he commented, "You'll have me in the hills here, making a right turn." At this point the controller's instruction was to " . . . climb and maintain 4,000 (1,220 m), return to the Riverside VOR, execute the VOR approach . . . " The wreckage was found the day after the accident at 4,500 feet (1,370 m) on the south slope of a canyon, approximately 16 miles (26 km) north-northwest of the destination airport. There were no survivors and intensive ground fire followed impact.

The NTSB determined that . . . "the probable cause of this accident was the radar vectoring of the aircraft below terrain clearance level following target misidentification by the FAA controller!"

Case III: MIDAIR COLLISION[38]   Near Milwaukee, summer, 1968

The private pilot of a high-wing lightplane took off at 9:00 a.m. from an airport at Lombard, Illinois, west of Chicago. With him were two passengers and the planned destination was given as Sheboygan, Wisconsin, 120 miles (192 km) to the north. The flight was conducted under Visual Flight Rules (VFR) without a filed flight plan. There was no known radio contact with any ground station during the flight.

A twin-engine turboprop transport took off from O'Hare Airport near Chicago at 9:34 a.m. on an Instrument Flight Rules (IFR) flight plan to Milwaukee.

At 9:48 a.m. the two aircraft collided approximately 11.5 miles (18.5 km) southwest of General Mitchell Airport, Milwaukee, at an altitude of 2,700 feet (823 m). All major components of the lightplane fell to the ground, with the exception of the cabin section with its three occupants and the attached landing gear which were embedded in the transport's forward baggage compartment. Damage sustained by the transport was extensive, but controlled flight was maintained by the captain and a successful landing accomplished at General Mitchell Field at 9:54 a.m.

---

[38]NTSB Accident Report SA-405.

The three occupants of the lightplane were killed, and the first officer on the transport sustained serious injuries. The captain, stewardess, additional crewmember and eight passengers on board the transport were not injured.

At impact, the transport was on a heading of 356° and the lightplane was on a heading of 314°, thus forming a convergence angle of 42°. The indicated airspeed of the transport was approximately 190 knots, while that of the lightplane was calculated to be 80 knots. The rate of closure between the two aircraft was 143 knots. There was no way the lightplane pilot could have been warned of the fact that his intended flight path would intersect that of the transport.

At the time of the collision, the transport crew was in radio and radar contact with Milwaukee Approach Control, and the flight had been cleared to descend to 2600 feet (790 m) on a vector heading of 350° for an intercept with the Instrument Landing System (ILS) localizer course serving runway 7R.

During the two minutes prior to the collision, the transport was issued three consecutive radar traffic advisories which described a target as "twelve thirty, four miles (6.5 km), northbound," then "one o'clock, three miles, northbound," and finally, "one o'clock, a mile and a half, north-northwest bound." The transport flight crew searched for this target but were unable to sight it until immediately prior to impact when it was too late to take evasive action. Their detection efforts were hampered by a dense concentration of insect smears on the forward windshield and direct vision windows, which had accumulated at a heavy rate during the flight.

The surface weather observation made at 0920 at General Mitchell Field indicated visibility was 3 miles (4.8 km) in haze and smoke.

The NTSB determined the probable cause to be the inability of the transport flight-crew to detect the lightplane visually in sufficient time to take evasive action, despite having been provided with three radar traffic advisories concerning the latter aircraft. Visual detection capabilities were substantially reduced by the heavy accumulation of insect smears on the forward windshield and direct vision windows of the transport. Visibility was further reduced by haze, smoke and sun glare, and by the inconspicious color and lack of relative motion of the lightplane. Under these circumstances, the crew of the transport should have requested a radar avoidance vector.

These tragic cases involving the failures and limitations of both the human element and the electronic, point up the importance of continuing work on the accuracy, reliability and simplicity of the complete ATC/NAV system.

Airports

In the U.S. there are over 11,000 airports available to general aviation. Over 600 airports are well-equipped and are used by scheduled air carrier aircraft. These may present problems to the general aviation pilot with respect to traffic, wake turbulence, landing fees, and other matters. At the other extreme, however, almost 6,000 of the airports or airfields have less than 3,000 feet (915 m) of runway length. Obstacles such as trees, power lines, buildings and terrain may hamper approaches and takeoffs at the smaller fields and have been cause factors in accidents.

Following are examples of accidents typical of the airport environment, such as slippery runways and over-run, obstructions and wake turbulence:

Case I: SHORT WET RUNWAY   Missouri, spring 1970

The Colorado pilot of a single-engine, high-wing airplane with his wife and three small children aboard made a precautionary landing in rain on a 2,000-foot (610 m) hard-surface runway to avoid a thunderstorm. According to a witness, the airplane touched down about three-quarters of the way down the runway and "appeared to hydroplane the rest of the way." It continued off the end of the runway and went up on its nose, sustaining substantial damage. There were no injuries.

Here a combination of imminent severe weather, family responsibility, a strange airport and a short wet runway combined to cause an accident, fortunately without harm to the participants. Greater runway length, better drainage and greater traction would have avoided an accident.

Case II: OBSTRUCTIONS   Florida, summer 1965

The pilot, with 520 total hours, flying a small experimental biplane, touched down on the 2,750 feet (840 m) long, 50 feet (15 m) wide runway. There was an 8 to 10 left crosswind. During roll-out, the airplane veered to the right, off the runway and into weeds three to four feet (.9 to 1.2 m) high. The airplane flipped completely over but came to rest in an upright position. The pilot sustained serious injuries.

Keeping the area around the runway free of obstacles improves safety.

91

A four-place single-engine, low-wing aircraft, flying under Visual Flight Rules on a business trip, had been cleared by the San Francisco tower to land behind an airline 707. When the pilot of the small aircraft reported to the tower that he was passing Coyote Point on his final approach, about 1.5 miles (2.4 km) behind the 707, the tower cleared him to land on runway 28 with this warning, " . . .caution wake turbulence from the aircraft just landed. . . " The pilot did not acknowledge.

An airline pilot witness said the small aircraft was low and about a mile (1.6 km) behind the 707 at Coyote Point. Soon thereafter it rolled onto its back and crashed into San Francisco Bay about one-half mile (0.8 km) short of the airport. The 2,831-hour pilot and his lone passenger were killed.

The NTSB determine the probable cause to be vortex turbulence due to failure to follow approved procedures.

Some measure of the intensity of wake vortex may be gained from the photograph on page 93, taken after passage of a large transport along a test course.

The Airport and Airway Revenue Act of 1970 imposing a fuel tax as a user charge was intended to provide funds, among other things, for airports for general aviation. However, recent proposals on revenue-sharing wherein federal funds for transportation are returned to the states without specific stipulation as to their use may result in less than the expected government support for general aviation airports.

Further, the cost of real estate in major metropolitan areas has forced many general aviation airports out of existence, with a reduction in the number of potential users. Growing opposition by citizens associations to all airports continues to hamper the development of airports for general aviation, particularly those located close to populated areas. As a result, general aviation must increasingly use remote airfields, or busy metropolitan airports where it is not wanted nor where its pilots want to be. Both safety and utility would be improved if government and the public were to develop a more open-minded and constructive approach to the provision of airports.

Apparently, there is little realization of the potential benefits. General aviation airports were purposely constructed in 84 of Ohio's 88 counties. The State invested $6.2 million in 62 airports, limiting its allocation to $100,000 to each airport. As a result, the Ohio Department of Developments has traced the following benefits directly to these airports:

---

[39]NTSB Release SB 70-60.

WAKE TURBULENCE

This photograph shows the intensity of the tip vortices generated by a low-level fly-by of a jet transport in a test at the FAA National Aviation Facilities Experimental Center (NAFEC) at Atlantic City, New Jersey.

- Sixty thousand new jobs were added.
- An additional $250 million in personal income was generated.
- Enough trade was generated to support 200 retail establishments.
- Fifteen hundred manufacturing firms were added or expanded.
- Within one year after an airport was completed, the value of the adjacent land had risen 100%.
- Twenty new industrial parks were established.

The State of Minnesota, like Ohio, has demonstrated that the airport can serve as a tool by which society can improve itself. Minnesota, having one of the best small-airport systems in the country, has used it to stimulate industrial growth in many small communities.

The super-highway has improved both the speed and safety of automobile travel so that it is a serious competitor of general aviation for the door-to-door travel market of an increasing number of people. In it, however, lies a possible solution to cost and accessibility problems of general aviation airports. It was the late William Piper who proposed the incorporation of landing strips along major highways close in to metropolitan centers. With very little additional cost in right-of-way, grading or paving, such facilities could be installed, and their proximity to surface travel would shorten the door-to-door time.

Guidance for approach and landing, and particularly vertical guidance, is important to all airports, including general aviation. Ground-based electronic and visual aids such as ILS and VASI systems are installed at some general aviation airports, and airborne aids such as glide slope computers and visual approach monitors are also in the development stage. General aviation overshoots result in an average of 315 accidents per year, or almost one per day. Under-shoots average 186 accidents per year, or one every other day.

Air carrier aircraft are plagued less by this problem as they overshoot to an accident only twice a year and undershoot to an accident four times a year. The lower air carrier undershoot/overshoot rate speaks highly of professional crews, and perhaps also indicates that they know when to "go around" and are not too proud to do so. Be that as it may, the point is that undershoots and overshoots could be virtually eliminated with vertical guidance to the runway—electronic for IFR and visual for VFR.

A low-cost approach light system of a type now coming into use for general aviation airports is shown on page 95. With it, for contrast, is shown a current installation with a standard support arrangement.

LOW COST APPROACH LIGHT SYSTEM

FAA-NAFEC

STANDARD APPROACH LIGHT SYSTEM

The Aircraft

Unlike the human element and weather, much has been done and much more can be done to the aircraft to improve safety. Most of these improvements will come in an evolutionary way through changes made to aircraft in production and as new types are designed, tested and put into production. Some developments can be incorporated into existing aircraft or into the production lines of current aircraft. Research aircraft embodying new principles demonstrate the potential of new concepts and facilitate the judgments on any changes and/or compromises that must be made to produce an improved operational aircraft.

Armstrong has pointed out that[40] "general aviation aircraft is a neglected area from the research viewpoint and the need is accentuated by the sheer number in operation, the large number of pilots, the increasing complexity of the aircraft and flight procedures, and the existing accident rate which is much higher than for other classes of aircraft." NASA expects to step up its efforts in general aviation technology with emphasis on easing pilot workload through improved controls, better knowldege of the characteristics and response of general aviation aircraft to turbulence and wake vortices, improved instrumentation and more economical propulsion through technology leading to low-cost gas turbine engines.

As discussed earlier, the aircraft and equipment designer and builder must constantly strive to produce machines offering greater "hands-off" stability while also being more directly responsive to the pilot and more tolerant of his mistakes. They also should present him with information as to his attitude, speed, direction and location in the most direct manner.

Principal areas holding promise of improvements include the following:

Stall Spin — As shown on page 46, failure to maintain flying speed is the primary cause of accidents. An NTSB study[41] shows that stall/spin accidents, some 578 cases, were the leading type of fatal or serious accident, during the period of the study — the years 1966, 1967 and 1968. Here is a fertile field for improvement in safety that aerodynamic research and application of the results of research can assist. Airfoils without a sharp break in the maximum lift value or the incorporation of leading edge devices would assist in eliminating or "softening" the stall. The use of counter-rotating propellers in light twin-engine airplanes has been found to improve stall characteristics. Further, the use of spoilers or floating ailerons, powerful devices at low speed, for lateral control, the possibility of adapting boundary layer control, limitation of the rearward travel of the center of gravity and

[40] Armstrong, Neil A. – Report to U.S. House Committee on Science and Astronautics – January 1971.
[41] C.O. Miller, Paul Alexander, Starke Jett, U.S. General Aviation Safety Record, SAE, Wichita, March 26, 1971.

the use of stick-pushers also are among possible ways of reducing stall/spin accidents.

Two examples, the one on accelerated stall on page 84 and the one below on the all-too-common attempt to turn back, highlight the stall/spin problem.

Case I: STALL-SPIN[42]   England, summer, 1969

An American pilot took off from Halfpenny Green aerodrome in a small U.S.-built "midget" Mustang-type experimental airplane to check the operation of a newly installed engine, propeller and fuel system, for the English owner to whom he had sold the airplane. On reaching an altitude between 50 and 100 feet (15 - 30 m) and covering a total horizontal distance of nearly 2,000 feet (600 m), the engine cut out. The aircraft went into a steep left turn during which it suddenly rolled to the left over on its back, remained inverted for a moment, and then rolled to the left again. It side-slipped into the ground in a nose and left-wing-down attitude, with a high rate of descent and low forward speed.

From the point of impact the aircraft skidded 66 feet (20 m) along an intersecting runway and was seriously damaged, but there was no fire. The pilot was severely injured and died in a hospital a few hours later.

The investigators concluded that the "forced landing, which was inevitable after an engine failure at such a low altitude, might well have been accomplished successfully if carried out straight ahead on the remaining runway and largely unobstructed overshoot area beyond. Since no defects could be found which would adversely affect the aircraft's handling characteristics, it seems probable that the steep left-hand turn was the result of a deliberate action by the pilot to turn back towards the runway. To try to account for his attempting such a potentially dangerous maneuver, it must be remarked that he had considerable experience in the airplane and similar types of aricraft and had succeeded on at least one previous occasion in saving an aircraft following an engine failure after takeoff, by making a reciprocal turn back to the runway. It is very possible that having succeeded before, the thought of again saving an aircraft from damage was uppermost in his mind."

Prior to this flight, a number of engine runs were conducted to maximum static rpm to check operation and fuel flow in the gravity feed system. This test was inadequate, however, in view of the higher rpm and fuel demand in flight as well as a lower fuel pressure head because of the greater

[42] British Board of Trade Report No. CAP 338, 1970.

97

fuselage angle in flight. Fuel quantity was approximately three gallons (13.6 liters) at the time of the flight. A rubber sliver obstruction in the fuel line was found to have been the cause of the engine failure through reduction in fuel flow.

The pilot was using both seat belt and shoulder harness but the investigators also found that the "accident might well have been survivable if the safety harness lapstrap had not broken due to an inadequate repair."

This is the almost classic accident type wherein the steep turn close to the surface ends in a stall-spin. Continuing straight ahead would have resulted in little or only moderate damage. In the clear light of hindsight, four errors compounded a fatality: improper assembly of a fuel line, an inadequate flow test, a decision to turn back to the field, and inadequate repair of a seat belt.

While this accident was found to have resulted from pilot action in an amateur-built experimental airplane, a "soft-stall" or "flat-top lift curve" type of airfoil, with and possibly without better lateral control, probably would have avoided this fatal accident. Instead, the airplane might have settled or "mushed" into the ground with no more than moderate injuries to the pilot.

Stability. Another major factor in flight safety is aircraft stability, particularly to the extent that the aircraft may be flown "hands off." This degree of stability can be obtained by aerodynamic means alone, as attested by the many small flying model aircraft. However, in full scale such aircraft generally are unpleasant to fly and exhibit a propensity for changing heading, roll attitude, etc., in rough air. Further, they frequently display dutch roll instability. Civil aircraft are required to have longitudinal (pitch) and directional (yaw) stability, but lateral (roll) stability is required only while holding a specific heading. Many aircraft if left unattended will enter an increasingly steep and tight spiral dive; that is, they have "spiral instability." For this reason devices such as "wing-levelers" and other stability augmentation devices have been developed for light aircraft by industry and FAA.[43] Comprehensive flight tests of the latter device in a Beech Debonair, similar to the one shown on page 102 by Cornell Aeronautical Laboratory, under both VFR and IFR task conditions using 26 non-instrument rated pilots showed that it "significantly improved the non-instrument rated pilot's ability to maintain control of the airplane during an inadvertent encounter with IFR conditions".[44]

The combination of an aerodynamically clean airplane, spiral instability, and a marginally proficient pilot can cause accidents in night and IFR

---

[43] Charles K. Jones, Limited Flight Evaluation of Tactair Fluid Control Stability Augmentation Safety System NASA Tech. Memo SX-1284, June 1966.

[44] F.F. Eckhart, G.W. Hall, P.A. Martino. Flight Evaluation of a Stability Augmentation System for Light Airplanes, FAA Report ADS-83, November 1966.

conditions. It should be possible, through design, to combine an air brake and devices to insure spiral stability which, like wing flaps, could be operated when needed to provide "hands off" stable flight through the conditions mentioned above. Shaping of the aileron tips, use of aileron tabs adjustable to a negative dihedral, or even adjustable dihedral wing tips are possible methods.

In 1967 the FAA sought the comments of interested parties as to whether all light aircraft should be required to have spiral-stability or lateral stability augmentation devices. Late in 1970 the FAA withdrew the notice[45] since most comments indicated opposition to the devices because "they have not been sufficiently substantiated by operating experience and that such devices would give inexperienced pilots a false sense of security in deteriorating weather." Despite this rather pessimistic rating and without the force of regulation, the use of improved stability means is increasing.

Continuing work in stability augmentation should result in simple, low-cost systems providing substantial improvement in operating safety.

Handling Qualities. A comprehensive test program on the stability and control of a number of general aviation aircraft, both single and twin-engine types, was conducted by NASA.[46] The work was summarized as:

"The quantitative portion of this program indicated that the aircraft, as a class, have generally satisfactory stability and control characteristics. However, these characteristics are degraded with decreasing airspeed, increasing aft center of gravity, increasing power, and extension of gear and flaps.

"The qualitative portion of the program showed that the handling qualities are generally satisfactory during visual flight and during instrument flight in smooth air. Atmospheric turbulence degrades these handling qualities, with the greatest degradation noted during instrument landing system approaches. Such factors as excessive control-system friction, low levels of static stability, high adverse yaw, poor dutch roll characteristics, and control-surface float combine to make precise instrument tracking tasks, in the presence of turbulence, difficult even for experienced instrument pilots.

"The program revealed three characteristics of specific airplanes that are considered unacceptable if encountered by the inexperienced or unsuspecting pilot: (1) a violent elevator force reversal at reduced load factors in the landing configuration, (2) power-on stall characteristics that culminate in rapid rolloffs

---

[45] FAA Notice of Proposed Rule Making, No. 67-32.
[46] Barber, M.R. et al, An Evaluation of the Handling Qualities of Seven General Aviation Aircraft. NASA TN D-3726, November 1966.

99

and/or spins, and (3) neutral-to-unstable static longitudinal stability at aft center of gravity.

"A review of existing criteria indicated that the criteria have not kept pace with aircraft development in the areas of dutch roll, adverse yaw, effective dihedral, and allowable trim changes with gear, flaps, and power. This study indicated that criteria should be specified for control-system friction and control-surface float."

Engine failure at low speed in multi-engine airplanes has always presented a problem, both in performance and in control. Some years ago automatic feathering systems were developed to rapidly eliminate windmilling propeller drag, and to eliminate the human error of feathering the wrong propeller. There may be merit in developing automatic rudder displacement interaction for the latter purpose.

Further improvement in handling qualities may be expected as industry, FAA and NASA continue to work on the problems.

Minimum Speed. As Dressler[47] had pointed out:

"The statistical relationship between landing accident rate and average landing speed is strongly nonlinear. An independent study of all U.S. Air Force landing accidents, with more statistical reliability, shows that the correlation is very high, and that the relationship is actually cubic."

Regardless of whether the relationship is direct or cubic in civil aviation, it is reasonable to conclude that safety is improved as contact speeds are reduced; there is more time for pilot action and impact severity is reduced.

Some possible aspects of the effect of minimum speed on safety were discussed earlier *(page 41)* where it was shown that typically the average twin has double the wing loading of a single-engine airplane, hence lands some 40% faster. Statistics show that when accidents do occur to twin-engine airplanes, on the average they are more severe.

In the years following World War I, civil aviation grew rapidly and airplanes were operated successfully despite the lack of airports, navigation aids and weather information. A major factor in the relative safety of operation of that period, using pastures and strips along roads, was low minimum speed.

Wing loadings were in the 6- to 10-pound per square foot [psf] (29 to 49 kg/m²) range and the landing speed seldom exceeded 40 mph (64 kmh);

---

[47]Dressler, R.F. – New Approach to Air Safety Statistics. 19th Annual International Air Safety Seminar 1966, Flight Safety Foundation.

landing into a little breeze brought this down to around 30 mph (48 kmh). The reports of the testing of the replicas of very early aircraft contained in Wheeler's book[48] also illustrated the advantage of low minimum speed.

Obviously, there are limitations. The Curtiss Tanager,[49] winner of the Guggenheim Safe Aircraft Competition in 1929, with a wing loading of 8.5 psf (42 kg/m^2) sustained major damage due to wind gusts during a slow-flight demonstration. It is of interest, however, that this airplane in the Competition flight tests, equipped as it was with the early slots and flaps of that period, cleared a 35-foot (11 m) barrier in 500 feet (152 m) from start of roll on takeoff, flew at a minimum speed of 30 mph (48 kmh), and in landing, stopped in 295 feet (90 m) from the base of the 35-foot (11 m) landing barrier. Of interest from the standpoint of stability, as discussed earlier (page 98), was the test finding that the Tanager "will fly at any air speed from 45 to 100 mph (72-161 kmh) at any throttle opening for five minutes in gusty air, hands off controls." The Tanager is shown on page 102.

Current airworthiness standards, as shown in *Figure 1,* permit stall speeds up to 70 mph (113 kmh) for single-engine airplanes.

Performance. Among the most difficult airplanes to fly are those which are marginal in power. While statistics are not available at this time, there is evidence to indicate that increasing the power in the pre-World War II lightplanes from the original 37- to 40-hp engines up to 50 and 65 hp with improved power loading increased safety. Stall-spin accidents and collision with trees and other obstacles on takeoff were decreased.

Propulsion. The air-cooled flat engine using gasoline, employed in most general aviation aircraft, has been developed to a remarkably efficient and reliable degree. Further, continuing developments in the powerplant field hold a substantial potential for improvement in general aviation safety and efficiency. Miller[41] shows that in the period 1966-68, 498 or 21% of the accidents involving fatal or serious injury were associated with "engine, i.e., powerplant system failure or malfunction." However, this includes accidents associated with the human element such as running out of fuel, turning the selector valve to an empty tank, failure to use carburetor heat, etc., or broken exhaust valves, fatigue failure of a propeller, and other mechanical causes.

Figure 18 shows that in an accident where there is post-crash fire there is a much greater possibility of fatality. In a recent paper on aviation fuels Ogston[50] observed that,

[48]Wheeler, Building Aeroplanes for Those Magnificent Men/Foulis, 1965.
[49]Osborn, R.R. The Tanager and Some of Its History. Aviation Magazine, February 8, 1930.
[50]Ogston, A.R., Aviation Fuels and Their Safety Aspects, FSF 16th Annual Corporate Aircraft Safety Seminar, April 1971.

CURTIS TANAGER
Winner of the Guggenheim
Safe Airplane Competition of 1929

BEECH DEBONAIR
(Bonanza 33)

"When Orville and Wilbur Wright designed the first successful powered airplane 68 years ago, the only type of powerplant that could then be built with an adequate power-to-weight ratio was an adaptation of an automobile engine which required volatile gasoline as its fuel. The success of the Wright brothers and the many other pioneers who followed them in this country and in Europe set the pattern for the aircraft powerplant and the type of fuel, i.e., gasoline, for the next fifty years and more. However, had an enlightened government at that time funded a research study by a commission composed of scientists and engineers, to advise with regard to the best type of powerplant and fuel to be used by a passenger-carrying flying machine which in due course was to have a minimum control speed of around 80 miles per hour or more, it is certainly questionable whether the commission would have recommended a reciprocating piston engine depending on a high-tension electrical ignition system and having to use one of the most volatile and flammable liquid fuels available, namely, gasoline!

"Prior to World War II, prompted by Navy interest in finding a safer fuel than gasoline for use on aircraft carriers and also encouraged by serious interest on the part of Pan American Airways, American Airlines and doubtless others, refining processes were evolved, supported by a U.S. Navy research and development contract, to produce high-octane aviation gasoline with a flash point and volatility similar to that of kerosene. It was called 'Safety Fuel' and experimental batches of 90 octane and even 100 octane grades with a flash point above 100° F were tested by the Navy."

Unfortunately, there were certain problems which at the time (1936-40) defied practical solution. The low volatility of Safety Fuel required direct injection in place of the carburetor and no satisfactory direct injection system for spark ignition engines had been developed prior to World War II. Even with direct injection, starting at low temperatures required auxiliary heating.

The advent of the turbine engine in the early 1940's opened the way to the use of low-volatility fuels such as kerosene and a reduction in the fuel-fire hazard.

While the turbine has taken over almost completely in air carrier operation, there is considerable doubt among aircraft producers and designers as to whether the turbine engine, in the next 10 to 20 years, will power an appreciable portion of new production general aviation aircraft. The reason is cost. At this time the shaft turbine costs more than four times as much per horsepower as a piston engine, and there does not appear to be much

103

possibility of any large reductions in cost of the turbine. New types of engines, such as the Wankel, may be used but considerable time may pass before such engines are developed, tested and produced in sufficient quantities to replace an appreciable portion of piston engines in general aviation.

There is, however, a possibility that coming piston engines may be capable of using low-volatility fuels. The emphasis on emission control to reduce atmospheric pollution by motor vehicles has led to considerable research and development on fuel injection systems. The results of this work as applied to the development of changes to aviation piston engines, might permit the use of lower volatility fuels, and hence improve safety. In addition, fuel injection should reduce the incidence of powerplant icing.

Furthermore, if break-throughs did occur in the production and cost reduction of turbine engines, it would serve the same safety objective by permitting the use of safer low-volatility fuels.

Another phase of basic engine development holds promise of safety gains. This is to increase power, and particularly thrust at low speed, without adding weight. Since power tends to decrease stability this obviously must not be done at the expense of stability. While the gas turbine has provided a major improvement in engine power-to-weight ratio, considerable gain also may be expected from new types of piston engines using gearing and high rotational speed to obtain maximum power per displacement and weight unit while at the same time holding down propeller shaft speed. The lower shaft speed facilitates the use of larger diameter propellers, to the extent compatible with cruising speed requirements, and hence increases thrust at low forward speed to provide improved takeoff and climb performance. Increased power also would permit the use of pumps for boundary layer control to effect a reduction in minimum flight speeds and provide improved controllability.

Improvement in fuel containment under impact conditions, as discussed earlier (Chapter 8), and the separation of fuel from sources of ignition can materially decrease fatalities and injuries in accidents.

Cases involving fire and fatalities in what would otherwise be survivable accidents are herein briefed. Note that with one exception these occurred in the takeoff or climb phase. Both forward and vertical speed may have been low but the spillage of fuel together with the ignition potential of an engine at takeoff power combined to produce a fire. The occupants in some cases made their way out of the wreckage only to succumb later as a result of their burns.

Case I: CRASH FIRE   Pennsylvania, summer 1970

The pilot, accompanied by his son age 8 and two other boys age 13 and 14, took off in a rented low-wing airplane from a small airport for a short sight-seeing flight. The takeoff was made from a 1,900-foot (580 m) turf strip with an uphill slope for the first 800 to 1,000 feet (244-305 m). The "grass was approximately 4 inches (10 cm) long and there were soft spots with standing water on both sides of the runway."

While there were no witnesses to the accident, a lady in her yard a quarter of a mile (400 m.) from the crash site heard the crash and saw the fire but trees blocked her direct view of aircraft departing the airport. The aircraft came to rest in a clump of trees approximately 1,000 feet (305 m) from the end of the runway and to the left of an extended centerline.

All major components of the aircraft were found in the immediate vicinity of the crash site. The cabin area was consumed by fire and the youngest boy was dead on the scene. The others were outside the aircraft and were reported in the initial newspaper accounts to be in critical condition from burns. These subsequently proved fatal.

Case II: CRASH FIRE   New York, winter 1968

A light twin-engine airplane, being used in scheduled air taxi operation, took off with a small amount of cargo. On board were a qualified pilot in the right seat and a copilot with some 740 logged hours occupying the left seat in a training capacity. A senior pilot was in the rear seat as a passenger riding to the planned destination. As a training check the left engine was throttled after the gear was retracted and shortly thereafter "the right engine quit." In the descent, initial contact was made with the top of a large tree in a city park. The second contact was with another large tree located 89 feet (27 m) beyond the first tree. Ground impact was found to be approximately 27 feet (8 m) further along the wreckage path.

The major portion of the wreckage came to rest in the middle of a main street. During the final few feet of travel along the ground, the aircraft struck a station wagon.

The copilot and the passenger survived the impact, but were severely burned. The latter remained conscious after the accident and described the events during the flight. Both succumbed later.

Case III: CRASH FIRE   Michigan, summer 1970

The accident report indicated the pilot had inadvertently landed at the wrong airport — a private farm strip. When he learned of his mistake, he attempted a takeoff but aborted. He then deplaned three passengers and again attempted to take off. Witnesses stated that although the aircraft was in a nose-high attitude, it was not gaining altitude. The aircraft reached a height estimated as 25 feet (8 m) above the ground, then struck near the top of a tree just beyond and to the left of the strip, crashed and burned. Witnesses also stated the aircraft was attempting to take off to the east although the wind was from 290° to 300° at 5 to 8 mph (8 to 13 kmh). The length of the runway was 1,400 feet (426 m) with an additional 400 feet (122 m) overrun available to the east. The pilot received burns over 65% of his body. He did recover.

Case IV: CRASH FIRE[51]   New York, spring 1970

A low-wing monoplane, powered by two radial engines, took off on a scheduled air taxi operation (FAR Part 135) from a 6,300-foot (1,910 m) runway, with a crew of two and nine passengers. After attaining an altitude variously estimated between 25 and 75 feet (8-23 m), the airplane settled rapidly back toward the runway. The airplane landed, with the landing gear retracted, near the end of the takeoff runway. Initial ground contact, some 640 feet (195 m) from the end of the runway, was not severe, as indicated by the propeller marks which extended for more than 300 feet (92 m). The airplane skidded off the end of the runway, proceeded down a sharp incline, passed through components of the approach light system and stopped almost 400 feet (122 m) beyond the end of the runway. Fire consumed the fuselage and wing butt areas.

Three passengers exited through a break in the fuselage and the copilot made his way out through the opening in his window which had separated on impact. The remaining four passengers used the main entry door which broke open as the aircraft decelerated. The pilot and two of the passengers died in the wreckage.

The takeoff had been made under limited visibility and moderate snowfall conditions, temperature around freezing and snow was adhering to the wing.

---

[51]NTSB Safety Release SB 70-55, July 1970.

Shortly after midnight an experienced pilot with commercial and instrument ratings, in a rented four-place low-wing airplane with his wife as the only passenger, overshot the 2,500-foot (763 m) runway. The airplane struck telephone lines, fell to the ground, and ended up against railroad tracks as shown in the illustration on page 109.

The aircraft caught fire. Although the pilot was only slightly injured, his wife suffered severe burns.

Landing Gear. From the discussion on page 20, it can be seen that for all types of flying, instructional flying contributes the second highest number of total accidents − 993, or 20%. However, these accidents generally are less serious, since instructional accidents contribute only 9% of the total fatal accidents. The landing phase contributes a significant portion of all instructional accidents.

Considering the mechanical aspects, landing gear accident causes are, in order of frequency, 1) braking systems, 2) retracting systems, and 3) gear locking systems.

The tricycle gear introduced into civil aviation in the late 1930's proved to be a great advance over the earlier tail-wheel type. Subsequent refinements have made it an extremely reliable part of the aircraft.

However, if use of the airplane is to increase, using less highly skilled and coordinated pilots, there is more to be done. Two of the main problem areas in landing are 1) flare to reduce the sink rate, and 2) landing in crosswinds.

With the increasing use of high-lift devices, i.e., large flaps, leading edge devices, and the potential for pressure or suction boundary layer control to reduce landing speed, the landing flare could be eliminated if adequate energy absorption were provided. The Tanager of 1929 *(page 102)* had a landing gear wheel travel of 20 inches (51 cm) and could absorb the energy of impact of a 12 fps (3.7 m/s) sink rate. Additional shock absorption travel and capacity would provide a major step toward a simplified landing technique.

The principles of the tricycle gear are now well-understood and the advantages of a wide spacing for ground stability have been generally adopted. However, general aviation aircraft will be forced to an increasing degree to utilize single-strip runways and the crosswind problem will become more critical. An adaptation of the crosswind gear shows promise; the axle for the main gear wheels is mounted on a vertical swivel axis, and the main

---

[52]The Evening Star, Washington, D.C. July 16, 1971.

wheels may "toe-out" under spring restraint. Stops prevent "toe-in." When landing in a crosswind, the downwind wheel is subjected to the higher force, in some cases high enough to cause overturning, "wheel barrowing" or ground looping, an action sometimes aggravated by the nose wheel steering linkage or the pilot's action.

With the arrangement described here, wherein the downwind wheel "toes-out," the side load is relieved and the transverse motion is decreased as the upwind gear touches down and reduces the lateral drift.

Equipment. In the aircraft equipment area the most important improvement in safety undoubtedly would be the development of a low-cost attitude indicator which would closely simulate VFR conditions. As discussed earlier *(page 45)* and also shown on page 83, pilot disorientation in weather is a frequent cause of accidents.

To simulate VFR conditions some form of "head-up" display would appear to be most logical, either a display projected on the windshield or a horizontal bar of substantial size mounted above the instrument panel and driven to simulate the motion of the horizon during pitch, roll and yaw.

Some preliminary work in this area by FAA[53] led to the following conclusions:

> Based on screening tests of 25 pilot candidates and subsequent flight tests with two versions of a simple Head-Up Display (HUD) to test the concept as an aid in reduced visibility, with six pilots who had shown difficulty in aircraft control under IFR conditions, it was concluded that:
>
> 1. There is a real need for an aid that a low-time pilot can use in changing course to get out of low visibility.
>
> 2. HUDs patterned on the concept of a simple aid to the inexperienced pilot provide marked improvement in safety of flight.
>
> 3. Only a brief period of familiarization is required to achieve improved flight control using a HUD.
>
> 4. The essential element of a HUD is that it provides an easy-to-read, real-world presentation in the pilot's normal forward-viewing of the direction of flight.
>
> 5. The total flight hours logged is not a good predictor of flight-control performance for the non-instrument rated pilot.

---

[53] FAA Report 71-28.

A SIMPLE FORM OF HEAD-UP DISPLAY

OVERSHOOT AND A SURVIVABLE FIRE

6. A basic HUD appears to be a feasible approach to the need for an aid to get out of low visibility.

One form of display is shown on page 109, and an airplane configuration to provide optimum outlook for the pilot is shown below.

Design-Induced Pilot Error. There is no question but that a less-than-optimum arrangement, location, configuration and operation of controls, switches, valves and other devices which the pilot uses in operating an aircraft, may contribute to pilot error. A comprehensive study of this problem was conducted by NTSB *(see reference 14, page 32),* and continuing attention to its lessons by designers can bring improved safety. Standardization consistent with latitude for progress also will help.

Maintenance and Servicing. As the variety of usage and the amount and nature of equipment carried in aircraft increases, it becomes increasingly difficult for the aircraft producer to keep the machine simple and the cost down. Also, maintenance and servicing become more complex. It is then a major challenge to the designer to cope with problems of insuring that only the proper fuel or other fluid is used, that parts cannot be assembled improperly, and maintenance can be readily accomplished. This must remain an important objective. Important aids here are adequate and easily understood manuals.

A RESEARCH AIRPLANE
The Cessna XMC

110

10. CONCLUSIONS AND A LOOK AHEAD

The preceding chapters have brought out these principal findings:

- In 1969 the U.S., with about 80% of the world's general aviation activity, had 130,806 aircraft and over 700,000 pilots who flew over 3 billion miles in 25 million hours. This activity spans all civil aviation except air carrier.

- General aviation is a statistical catch-all for the entire body of civil aviation except air carrier. As a result the safety record includes not only pleasure flying and business aviation but also aerial application, experimental testing and other activities.

- General aviation safety in the U.S. has improved, the fatality rate having dropped from 26 per 100 million passenger (occupant) miles in 1959 to less than 18 in 1966. After remaining almost unchanged from 1966 through 1969, additional improvement in safety was shown in 1970, with the number of fatalities (1,270) down 15% from 1969.

- The fatality rate in general aviation, 18 per 100 million passenger miles, is higher than automobile travel which ranges from 2.7 to 7.5 per 100 million vehicle miles, depending on the highway type. However, general aviation injures only one person for each two fatalities, 697 in 1969, while the automobile injures 27 for each fatality, over 1,500,000 injuries in 1969.

- In their order of frequency, the leading cause factors in general aviation accidents are:

  > pilot
  > weather, and
  > mechanical

- During the years 1966 and 1967, of the 57 different accident types defined by the NTSB, accidents involving

  > stall/spin/mush,
  > collision with ground or water,
  > collision with wire, poles, trees or
  > other objects, and
  > engine failure or malfunction

accounted for 70% of the serious injury accidents, 80% of the fatal accidents and 83% of the accidents involving fire after impact.

111

- Accidents wherein fire follows crash impact are increasing in frequency and the possibility of fatality is substantially greater than in similar accidents without crash fire. More complete and concise reporting of such accidents would aid in developing design changes and improved standards.

- There is no appreciable difference in accident rates between high-wing and low-wing airplanes.

- Multi-engine airplanes are less likely to be involved in an accident than single-engine types, but when they do occur, multi-engine airplane accidents are more likely to be fatal.

- Improvements in crashworthiness are needed, but care must be exercised in improving aircraft crashworthiness to avoid reduction in airworthiness.

- General aviation suffers increasingly from the threat of legal involvement. Legal formalities hamper the development and administration of aviation safety codes, and fear of accident liability action hampers the exchange of safety information.

All elements of general aviation require improvement to increase safety. In their order of importance, they are:

The pilot. Greater safety in general aviation must come through improving and maintaining the competence and discipline of the pilot by recurrent training. Highly important here are the standards, stature and remuneration of flight instructors.

Weather. Weather facilities, ground stations and pilots aloft must be utilized in a coordinated and automated manner to provide accurate, up-to-the-minute and easily visualized information to the pilot, both before and during flight.

All Traffic Control and Navigation. The comprehensive and intensive research and development work to improve the air traffic control and navigation system must include optimum use of developments in electronics and other fields in order to provide the pilot with more accurate and readily visualized information as to his location and traffic conditions.

The Vehicle. Aircraft manufacturers must make optimum use of research and development as well as production advances to assure better aircraft performance, stability and control as well as greater ease of handling, margins for error and lower minimum speeds.

Airports. General aviation airports are needed nearer to metropolitan centers. Air strips associated with super highways hold promise. Having separate runways at major airports would facilitate both air carrier and general aviation operations. Equally important, vertical guidance for landing at all airports would reduce accidents.

There is no question but that accident and fatality rates in general aviation could be reduced by as much as 50% by 1980 through an aggressive program to improve piloting, aircraft and equipment design, airports, air traffic control and navigation, weather information and crashworthiness.

How can an aggressive drive be mounted to improve safety in general aviation? Government safety regulations will be raised in time but these must always be based upon minimum acceptable standards. Government developmental contracts in many cases contain references and clauses and other legal "boiler-plate" barnacles to the extent that they deter some capable organizations from competing and reduce the initiative and originality of those who do.

Some form of direct private venture competition may hold promise. The Orteig prize for the first non-stop flight between Paris and New York, won by Lindbergh, is probably the most famous example. The Ford Reliability Tours of the late 1920's spurred interest and progress in aircraft, equipment and operations. The Guggenheim Safe Airplane Competition had some influence on aircraft design. The Bendix Trophy races and others helped. The CAA Texas A&M College agricultural airplane project (page 62) stimulated new developments. Can a new kind of competition bring the aircraft, the equipment and the average pilot together to generate new concepts in design, training and operation?

Effort is underway on all elements of general aviation; better training of the individual, improvements in airways and airports, in weather information and in the aircraft and its airborne equipment. There is a limitation on what the human element can be expected to do — reliably. The other elements must be designed to compensate for these limitations.

The appropriate system competition could bring real progress in safety and utility.

APPENDIX

The Sponsor

This study has been sponsored by Clayton J. Brukner of Troy, Ohio, in the interest of advancing the safety of general aviation and as a memorial to his schoolmate and lifelong associate Elwood James (Sam) Junkin (1896-1926). Messrs. Brukner and Junkin organized the Waco Aircraft Company of Troy, Ohio, and Mr. Brukner was President until his retirement. As he has written,

"The support is in memory of the struggling pioneering years which Sam Junkin and I spent in the 'folly' that eventually became known as General Aviation.

"Our paramount objective of safety in designing for operations with the heavy OX5 engine and the chance hayfield landing surface must have been successful to a great degree when I think of the many under-instructed pilots who survived a Waco era — including myself. Since aviation was eventually good to me, it is certainly appropriate for me to eventually reciprocate . . .

" . . . it was Sam who catalyzed the airplane building project which we performed in the basement boiler room of the old Manual Training Building of Battle Creek High School in 1915. I believe that the public school system of Battle Creek in both its academic and manual courses was the best of its period, when we could successfully pioneer in aviation without benefit of further formal education."

Upon graduation, Clayton Brukner and Sam Junkin chose exhibition flying as a stepping stone to airplane manufacturing, the principal result being the experience gained in building and rebuilding several Curtiss-type pushers. In 1916, the war spawned an aircraft manufacturing industry in the eastern states and these men worked in the plants of Curtiss, Aeromarine, Standard, and others.

After the armistice, Brukner and Junkin began several years of endeavor to develop their own design of an airplane for the market now known as general aviation. In 1923, after disappointing experiences in Buffalo, New York, Lorain and Medina, Ohio, they launched their very successful war surplus OX5-powered three-passenger biplane in Troy, Ohio, and incorporated The Advance Aircraft Company, the name being changed to Waco Aircraft Company in 1928.

Charles Lindbergh had ferried a number of Wacos to a St. Louis dealer and at the time of his historic flight to Paris in 1927 the OX5-engined Waco

114

was rolling out at the rate of six per day. When the supply of war-surplus engines became exhausted, open and closed-cabin models were designed around the new air-cooled radial engines and these airplanes achieved worldwide fame and popularity for ease of handling and good performance. Wacos placed first in races of various types and distances — including the Ford Reliability Tour in successive years before the race formula incorporated a credit for multiple engines. Between the World Wars, Waco became the largest builder of commercial airplanes and supplied several hundred of its UPF-7 trainers to the aerobatic phase of the wartime Civilian Pilot Training Program. Waco then developed the cargo and troop-carrying gliders produced for the U.S. Army Air Forces during World War II, and provided engineering services to 15 other manufacturers of these aircraft.

Elwood J. Junkin

"Sam" Junkin was born in 1896 at Drayton, North Dakota, the son of a machine shop operator who became a prominent agricultural industrial engineer. The family moved to Battle Creek, Michigan, in 1914, when the father was commissioned to design a farm tractor for a local company. Sam's early interest in aviation inspired a visit with this father to the Chicago Air Meet of 1912, that served as a stimulating influence. Throughout his career as constructor, engineer and pilot, he contributed much to aviation progress. Mr. Junkin died in 1926.

Clayton J. Brukner

Mr. Brukner was born in 1896 at Ravenna, Nebraska, the son of a hardware merchant and threshing machinery dealer who eventually became engaged in the manufacture of such machinery in Battle Creek, Michigan. Brukner's work as an electrician in a cereal factory furnished initial support for his aviation work with Mr. Junkin.

Mr. Brukner has been active in the civic affairs of Troy, Ohio, one of his most recent philanthropies being the hospital wing bearing his name. In 1968 he established and funded the Brukner Nature Center which is presently developing a long planned conservation and nature study facility on 150 acres of uniquely suitable land. Since his retirement in 1963, Mr. Brukner has conducted a specialty machine development operation on a hobby basis.

The Authors

Harold D. Hoekstra. Vice-President, Engineering, FSF, Mr. Hoekstra was educated in the public schools of Battle Creek, Michigan and with Arthur Sheldon, later an executive with Waco and Cessna, built his first airplane in 1920. He received his Bachelor of Science degree in Aeronautical Engineering from the University of Michigan in 1929. He was a designer and aeronautical engineer with Ford, Crosley, Curtiss and Stinson.

In 1937 he joined the predecessor of the FAA and advanced from aeronautical engineer to division chief. He was active in the development and administration of airworthiness standards and in safety research and development work on general aviation, transport and supersonic aircraft. Following retirement from FAA, he joined FSF in September 1970.

The author of many technical papers and reports, he is a Fellow of the Royal Aeronautical Society and of the AIAA and a member of the Society of Automotive Engineers, and 1970 Chairman of the SAE Engineering Activity Board. He is a registered professional engineer in the District of Columbia and a member of the Society of Air Safety Investigators.

Mr. Hoekstra soloed in 1930 and is an active pilot with a current commercial pilot rating.

Shung-chai Huang. Director, Statistics Division, FSF, Mr. Huang received his early education in the public school of Kwangtung Province, China, and his B.A. Degree in Economics from National Chengchi University, Nanking, China in 1945. He came to the United States in 1959. In 1964-65, he did research work in Mathematics in the graduate school of Queens College, Flushing, New York.

Principal References

I   Federal Aviation Regulations, Title 14, Parts 1 through 200, U.S. Government Printing Office, Washington, D.C.

II˙   Annual Review of U.S. General Aviation Accidents, NTSB, Washington D.C. Annual Editions.

III   FAA Statistical Handbook of Aviation — Annual Editions, FAA, Washington D.C.

IV   Census of U.S. Civil Aircraft — Annual Editions, FAA, Washington D.C.

V   Accident Facts 1970 Edition, National Safety Council, Chicago, Illinois.

VI   The Magnitude and Economic Impact of General Aviation 1968-1980, R. Dixon Speas Associates, Manhasset, New York, 1970.

VII   Jane's All The World's Aircraft. Annual Editions.

VIII ICAO Bulletin — Monthly Issues, ICAO, Montreal, Canada.

LIST OF FIGURES

119

LIST OF ILLUSTRATIONS

INDEX

123

125